EDWARD SRI

NO GREATER LOVE

A BIBLICAL WALK THROUGH
CHRIST'S PASSION

ASCENSION

West Chester, Pennsylvania

Ascension
Post Office Box 1990
West Chester, PA 19380
1-800-376-0520
ascensionpress.com

Printed in the United States of America

ISBN 978-1-945179-74-7

CONTENTS

NO
GREATER
LOVE

INTRODUCTION

Welcome!

No Greater Love: A Biblical Walk Through Christ's Passion is more than a Bible study. It is a biblical pilgrimage that reveals Christ's amazing love for us. As you begin this journey, here is what you will need to get started.

Materials Needed

1. *No Greater Love* workbook – Contains engaging study questions (with session summaries, home reading assignments, and talk notes) and responses to the questions.

2. *No Greater Love* book – Contains text that will be used for the home preparation of each session.

3. A Catholic Bible – We recommend *The Great Adventure Catholic Bible.*

Every participant, study leader, and small-group facilitator will need their own workbook, book, and Bible.

4. *No Greater Love* video presentations (eight 30-minute sessions) – Filmed on location in the Holy Land, these engaging videos provide comprehensive teaching and commentary on Christ's passion. (Available online and on DVD.)

These materials can be purchased at **ascensionpress.com** or by calling **1-800-376-0520**.

How the Study Works

Every session in this study includes four essential steps, which are designed to fit together and build upon each other. Following these steps in order will allow you to get the most out of each session.

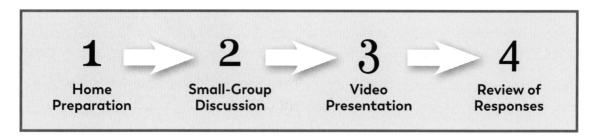

Step 1: Home Preparation

NOTE: There is no home preparation required for Session One.

Each session begins with personal study that involves reading Scripture and answering a series of questions that will help you understand and think more deeply about what you have read. Some questions will include additional readings from Ed Sri's book *No Greater Love: A Biblical Walk Through Christ's Passion* to help you dive deeper into the content.

We recommend that you allow at least 90 minutes to complete the reading and answer the questions for each session. We also suggest that home preparation be done in several sittings over the course of a week. This will help you create a habit of daily Bible reading and prayerful meditation.

Note: Although the responses to the questions are provided in the back of the workbook, the richness that comes from individual insights can be lost when participants view the responses prior to the discussion. Your small-group facilitator will incorporate the points made in the responses section during your discussion time when you meet.

Step 2: Small-Group Discussion

One of the richest parts of a Bible study is the small-group discussion. During this discussion, you and the other members of your small group will have the opportunity to share the insights you gained by reading the Scripture passages and answering the questions at home. This small-group discussion will allow you to obtain a richer understanding of these readings and will help you apply them to your life. Trained facilitators will guide the small-group discussions and keep them on track. Be sure to follow the "Ten Commandments of Small-Group Discussion" on page 5.

Step 3: Video Presentation

Edward Sri wraps up each session with a video presentation that offers unique insights and profound connections to help you gain a deeper understanding of Christ's passion and its relationship to the Catholic Faith and your life, with a special emphasis on ways to apply what you have learned to your life.

The study leader will conclude the session with the prayer provided at the end of each session.

Step 4: Review of Responses

The final step—reviewing the responses at the back of this workbook—is done at home prior to beginning the reading for the next session. These responses will help you read the Scripture passages for the next session in the proper context.

For the richest study experience, complete these steps in order: **(1)** Read and answer the questions; **(2)** discuss them in your small group; **(3)** view the video presentation; and **(4)** review the responses.

For more information about how to plan and promote a Bible study and how to facilitate a small-group discussion, visit ascensionpress.com or call 1-800-376-0520.

Session Outline

Each session in this workbook has the following sections.

1. Session Questions (used during Step 1: Home Preparation and Step 2: Small-Group Discussion.)

    A. Establish the Context

    B. Read the Story

    C. Take a Deeper Look

    D. Application

2. Session Talk Notes (used during Step 3: Video Presentation)

3. Session Responses (used by facilitators to prepare for Step 2: Small-Group Discussion and by participants at home in Step 4: Review of Responses)

What to Do for Each Session

1. Welcome and Introduction (10 minutes)

2. Small-Group Discussion (40 minutes)

    Note to Study Leaders: There is a shorter small-group discussion for the first week. This way you can use the additional time to divide participants into small groups of eight to twelve people, ensure that everyone has the study materials, and explain how the study works. Each small group should be led by a trained facilitator.

3. Video Presentation (30 minutes)

4. Closing and Prayer (5 minutes)

Getting the Most Out of This Study

This study will help you understand Christ's passion in a new way. The "head knowledge" you gain will help you grow in "heart knowledge" as you follow up on what you have learned. The Bible will always remain a mystery, though, and that is part of the beauty of it: We can never exhaust the treasures of Scripture. Fortunately for us, the Bible is not a subject to master; it is a place to encounter the living Word of God.

Whenever you open your Bible to read, start with prayer and place yourself in God's presence. You might take Samuel's prayer as your own: "Speak, Lord, for your servant is listening" (1 Samuel 3:10).

When you read, adopt an attitude of listening. Try not to treat Scripture as a text, but as a personal message from God. What is he saying? What does it mean? And what does it mean for my life? If you come to the Word focused on having an encounter with the Lord, he will speak to your heart, and you will be transformed.

Responses to the questions are provided in the back of this workbook to help facilitators prepare for the small-group discussion and for participants to review after the small-group discussion.

Participants should not review the responses for each session until after the session is completed. Although it might be tempting to look at these responses in advance, it is important to wait for the following reasons:

1. Bible study is not about simply watching a video presentation or reading a Bible commentary. It is just as important to immerse yourself in the Word of God itself and engage it with your heart and mind. The questions in this study are designed to draw you into the Scriptures so that the Word of God will be planted and grow in your heart. Reading a response written by someone else may satisfy your mind for a moment, but it will not result in the kind of growth that will occur if you attempt to answer the question on your own first.

2. The success of a small group depends on a good discussion. A group of participants who have spent time pondering the Scripture passages on their own will have more varied insights to discuss.

When you follow the steps of this study as intended, you will explore the Word of God in different ways: in the reading, the small-group discussion, the video presentation, and, finally, in the responses. Follow these steps over time and you will be more than fed; you will learn to feed yourself.

Ten Commandments of Small-Group Discussion[1]

1. Enjoy yourself!

2. Speak with respect and charity.

3. Do not ridicule or dismiss what others say. Keep comments positive.

4. Come prepared.

5. If you were not able to prepare, let others speak first.

6. Stick to the topic and questions at hand.

7. Start and end on time.

8. Allow silence. Give people a chance to think.

9. Listen to others without interrupting.

10. Keep personal matters within the group.

---

[1] Adapted from Thomas Smith's original "10 Commandments of a Small Group."

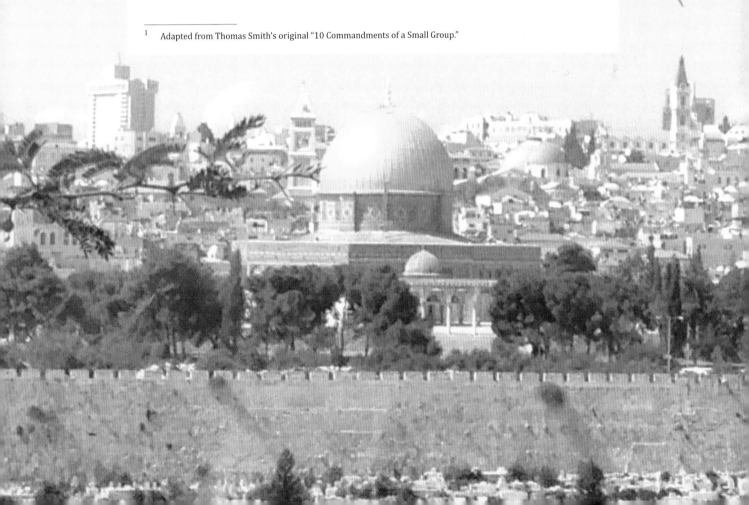

NO
GREATER
LOVE

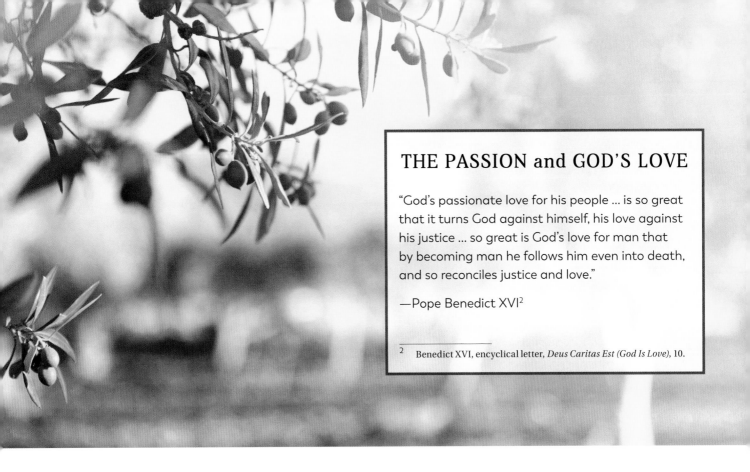

SESSION ONE

THE PRAYER OF THE AGONY

Jesus in Gethsemane

A. Establish the Context

Our biblical walk through Christ's passion begins on the Mount of Olives in the garden of Gethsemane, where Jesus came with his disciples to pray. Jesus had passed over this same mountain earlier this week when he entered Jerusalem riding a donkey. He had come here to pray at other times during his time in Jerusalem for the Passover feast. After celebrating his Last Supper, in which he gave us the gift of his Body and Blood in the Eucharist, he came back to this Mount of Olives once more to pray.

This time, things are very different. The Gospels immediately make it clear that Jesus' visit to Gethsemane on this night is no ordinary prayer time. Jesus is "greatly distressed," his soul is "very sorrowful even to death," and he falls to the ground on his face in prayer. We have never seen Jesus pray like this before (see Mark 14:33-35). As he prays in agony, his sweat becomes like drops of blood, and an angel comes to strengthen him (see Luke 22:43-44). Knowing all that was about to befall him at the moment as his final battle with the devil is about to begin, Jesus prays, "My Father, if it be possible, let this chalice pass from me; nevertheless, not as I will, but as you will" (Matthew 26:39).

B. Read the Story

This session focuses on the following verses that tell of Jesus' agony the in the garden of Gethsemane: **Matthew 26:36-46; Mark 14:32-42;** and **Luke 22:39-46.** You do not need to read these verses now, as you will be reading these accounts as part of your preparation for Session Two.

C. Take a Deeper Look

1. What inspires you most about Jesus' prayer in Gethsemane: "My Father, if it be possible, let this chalice pass from me; nevertheless, not as I will, but as you will" (Matthew 26:39)?

2. What do you think it means to do the Father's will and not your own? How does this prayer inspire you to do God's will more in your life?

D. Application

Reflect

In Gethsemane, Jesus surrenders perfectly to the Father's will when he prays, "Not as I will but as you will" (Matthew 26:39). What are some of the things that keep you from entrusting more of your life to the Father's plan for you? Is it fear? Not wanting to give up control? Not being convinced God is trustworthy? Not wanting to surrender your plans to his plans? Is there an area of your life for which you could seek his will more or entrust more to his hands?

Commit

In the Bible, God says, "For I know the plans I have for you, says the LORD, plans for welfare and not for evil, to give you a future and a hope" (Jeremiah 29:11). How might this verse give you confidence to seek and do the Father's will for your life, especially in that area? What can you do practically to live more like Jesus in that area and say, "Not as I will, but as you will" (Matthew 26:39)?

Pray

Pray the following prayer from St. Ignatius of Loyola. It's a prayer of surrender, entrusting one's entire life to God:

> "Take, Lord, and receive all my liberty,
> my memory, my understanding, and my entire will,
> all that I have and possess.
> Thou hast given all to me.
> To Thee, O Lord, I return it.
> All is thine; dispose of it wholly according to thy will.
> Give me Thy love and Thy grace,
> for this is sufficient for me."[3]

For more background on this session, see "Introduction" and chapters one through four in Edward Sri's book *No Greater Love: A Biblical Walk Through Christ's Passion.*

---

[3] St. Ignatius of Loyola, *Spiritual Exercises*, trans. Louis J. Puhl (Chicago: Loyola University Press, 1951), 192.

TALK NOTES

The Prayer of the Agony:
Jesus in Gethsemane

I. "Greater love has no man than this, that a man lay down his life for his friends" (John 15:13)

II. Holy Week

    A. Jesus enters Jerusalem riding on a donkey

    B. The Cleansing of the Temple

    C. The Last Supper

    D. The Passion

III. The Mount of Olives

    A. David and Jesus both crossed the Kidron Valley and prayed here (see 2 Samuel 15:13-31; Luke 22:39-46; John 18:1)

    B. David and Jesus were both betrayed by close friends, Ahithophel and Judas

    C. Both Ahithophel and Judas hanged themselves

    D. It is prophesied that the Lord would stand on the Mount of Olives (see Zechariah 14:4)

IV. The Great Battle

    A. The devil is the unseen dark force behind Jesus' passion

        1. After his temptation in the desert, the devil departed from Jesus "until an opportune time" (Luke 4:13)

        2. Jesus confronts the powers of darkness by

            a. raising people from the dead

            b. liberating people from their sins

            c. expelling demons

        3. Satan enters Judas, who betrays Jesus to the chief priests (see Luke 22:3-6)

        4. Jesus tells his disciples that Satan demands to have them and sift them like wheat (see Luke 22:31)

        5. Jesus says to his captors, "This is your hour, and the power of darkness" (Luke 22:53)

TALK NOTES

V. Sorrowful unto Death

    A. Jesus was "greatly distressed" (Mark 14:33, recalling Psalm 55:4)

    B. "My soul is very sorrowful, even to death" (Mark 14:34, recalling Sirach 37:2)

    C. "It is not a grief to the death when a companion and friend turns to enmity" (Sirach 37:2)

    D. "He fell on the ground and prayed" (Mark 14:35)

VI. The Garden of Gethsemane

    A. John's Gospel mentions there was a garden there (see John 18:1)

    B. *Gethsemane* (Aramaic): oil press

    C. The rock structure in the Church of All Nations is venerated as the site where Jesus came to pray

VII. The Angel and the Blood

    A. An angel came to strengthen Jesus (see Luke 22:43)

        1. An angel protected the three youths in the fiery furnace (see Daniel 3:26)

        2. An angel rescues the apostles from prison (see Acts 5:19; 12:6-11)

        3. An angel ministers to Jesus after his temptation in the desert (see Matthew 4:11)

    B. Jesus was in agony and his sweat became like drops of blood (see Luke 22:44)

VIII. Why Peter, James, and John?

    A. The same apostles Jesus brought to witness his Transfiguration (see Luke 9:28-36)

    B. The Transfiguration prepared the apostles for Christ's passion (see CCC 555)

IX. The Prayer of the Agony (see Matthew 26:39)

    A. Jesus is fully human and fully divine

    B. Jesus surrenders his human will to his Father's will and embraces his cross

X. "Watch and Pray" (Mark 14:38)

    A. To watch means to be vigilant

    B. Be on guard against the devil (see 1 Peter 5:8)

        1. Call on the name of Jesus

        2. Make the Sign of the Cross

        3. Call upon your guardian angel

        4. Watch and pray with Jesus in Adoration, especially on Holy Thursday

Judas Betrays Jesus With a Kiss (Fresco in the Collegiata of San Gimignana, Italy)

"ARE YOU THE CHRIST?"
(Mark 14:61)

Jesus' Arrest and Trial Before the Sanhedrin

A. Establish the Context

In the opening session, we saw the intensity of what Jesus faces when he begins his passion in the garden of Gethsemane. The Gospels make this clear with several details about what Jesus endured in this time of prayer. Knowing all that was about to befall him, Jesus is "greatly distressed" and his soul is "very sorrowful even to death" (Mark 14:34). He kneels and falls to the ground prostrate in prayer (see Luke 22:41). In his agony, his sweat becomes like drops of blood and an angel appears to strengthen him (see Luke 22:43-44). At the center of his agony is his prayer, "Father, if it be possible, let this chalice pass from me; nevertheless, not as I will, but as you will" (Matthew 26:39). We saw how the prayer reflects both his humanity—which would be repulsed by his betrayal, scourging, and crucifixion (*"let this chalice pass"*)—and his divinity: "not *as I will*, but as *you will*" (Matthew 26:39, emphasis added). Nevertheless, Christ's *human will* remains perfectly united to his *Father's will*. Jesus feels the full weight of what he is about to endure, but he still chooses to embrace the suffering for the sake of our salvation. And yet, he knows his disciples' wills are not as committed. They are about to be tested in the garden, too, so he warns them to be vigilant: "Watch and pray that you may not enter into temptation" (Mark 14:38).

11

Now we turn our attention to what happens next. Soldiers, police, captains, chief priests, and elders of the people come to arrest Jesus in Gethsemane. They are led there by Judas, who has betrayed his Master. They come with torches, lanterns, swords, and clubs. And they come in large numbers. We will see how Jesus is not taken by surprise. Nor is he taken by force against his will. The Gospels highlight how he is actually the one in charge during his arrest, and he freely allows the crowd to hand him over to the chief priests.

DID JUDAS REPENT?

Though sometimes translated as "repented," the actual Greek word Matthew uses to describe what was going on in Judas' heart is *metamelomai* (see Matthew 27:3). The word means having a change of feeling or a change with one's concern, which can be accompanied by sadness. It could be translated as "having changed with remorse." The idea is that Judas deeply *regretted* his actions.

Despite the seriousness of Judas' sin, it would not have kept him from reconciliation with Jesus if he simply had turned to God—if he *repented* and trusted in God's mercy. Instead, Judas merely *regretted* what he did. He focused on himself and his horrific crime.

Imagine being at Jesus' trial before the Sanhedrin. There is confusion and disarray. False testimonies are sought, and they are not consistent. The high priest stands up and presses Jesus to speak, but Jesus remains silent before his accusers. Only when the high priest puts Jesus under oath does he finally speak. He says something that makes the high priest tear his robes and the Sanhedrin charge him with blasphemy. They condemn him to death, slap his face, spit at him, blindfold him, and strike him saying, "Prophesy! Who is it that struck you?" (Luke 22:64). What did Jesus say that was so upsetting? All he did was refer to himself as "the Son of man seated at the right hand of Power and coming on the clouds of heaven" (Matthew 26:64). We will unpack the meaning of this statement, which is the turning point of the trial.

Finally, both Peter and Judas are unfaithful to Jesus on this night, and both recognize their sin. But why is one eventually reconciled to Christ and the other ends in despair and death? What is the difference between the way Peter and Judas respond to their sin, and what lessons can we take away for our own lives?

B. Read the Story

Read the following verses that tell of Jesus' arrest and hearing before the Jewish Sanhedrin: **Matthew 26:36-75; Mark 14:32-72; Luke 22:39-71; John 18:1-27.**

For more background on this session, see chapter six in Edward Sri's book
No Greater Love: A Biblical Walk Through Christ's Passion.

C. Take a Deeper Look

1. Read **Mark 14:42** and **John 18:1-6.**

   a. Does Jesus seem to be taken by surprise by Judas and those coming to arrest him? Who seems to be in charge in this scene of his arrest?

   b. Read **John 10:14-15, 17-18.** What might this tell us about the role Jesus will play when he is arrested and eventually crucified?

2. When the crowd comes to the garden looking for Jesus of Nazareth, Jesus responds, "I am he" (John 18:5), and they "drew back and fell to the ground" (John 18:4-6). Consider how this scene reveals a glimpse of Jesus' divine power.

   a. Read **Exodus 3:14.** How is the expression "I AM" used in this passage with Moses at the burning bush? And what might this tell us about Jesus' similar expression in Gethsemane, "I am he"?

   b. Read **Psalm 35:4** and **Psalm 56:9.** What might these verses tell us about the crowd turning back when they came to arrest Jesus?

   c. Read **Revelation 1:12-17.** Why does St. John fall to the ground? What might that tell us about the crowd falling down when they come to arrest Jesus in Gethsemane?

3. A new Isaac:

   a. Read **Genesis 22:1-18**. In what ways does this scene prefigure Jesus' last week of his life when he enters Jerusalem?

	What happens to Abraham and Isaac in these verses from Genesis 22?	How might Abraham and Isaac prefigure what happens to Jesus in his last week in Jerusalem?
Read **Genesis 22:2** and **John 3:16**		
Read **Genesis 22:3** and **Matthew 21:1-9**		
Read **Genesis 22:6** and **John 19:17**		
Read **Genesis 22:9** and **John 19:18; Acts 5:30**		

b. Notice how Matthew's account of Jesus in the garden of Gethsemane recalls what happened to Isaac on Mount Moriah:

	Isaac on Mount Moriah (Genesis 22)	Jesus on Mount of Olives (Matthew 26)
Read **Genesis 22:5** and **Matthew 26:36**	What does Abraham say to his men?	What does Jesus say to his disciples?
Read **Genesis 22:6** and **Matthew 26:47**	What does Abraham take for the sacrifice?	What do the men coming to arrest Jesus bring with them?
Read **Genesis 22:10** and **Mathew 26:51**	What does Abraham do with his hand?	What does one of the disciples do with his hand?
Read **Genesis 22:12** and **Matthew 26:50**	What does the angel tell Abraham not to do with the boy?	What does the crowd do with Jesus?

4. Matthew 26:62 notes that the high priest "stood up."

    a. Read the following verses. What do they tell us about those who have "risen" or "stood up" against the righteous?

        i. **Psalm 27:12**

        ii. **Psalm 35:11**

        iii. **Psalm 86:14**

    b. What might this background tell us about the high priest who "stood up" during Christ's trial, pressing him to answer?

5. Read **Matthew 26:63** and **Isaiah 53:7**. What does this prophecy from Isaiah tell us about Jesus' silence before Caiaphas?

6. Caiaphas says to Jesus, "I adjure you, by the living God, tell us if you are the Christ" (Matthew 26:63). Read **1 Kings 22:14-16** about a conversation between the king and the prophet Micaiah.

    a. When the king uses the language "I adjure you" in this passage, what is he wanting from Micaiah?

    b. When Micaiah uses the expression, "As the LORD lives," what is he emphasizing?

    c. And how might this shed light on why Jesus finally answers the high priest?

7. Jesus refers to himself as "the Son of man seated at the right hand of Power, and coming on the clouds of heaven" (Matthew 26:64). This is an allusion to the famous "son of man" prophecy in Daniel. Read **Daniel 7:13-14**.

    a.   What do you think Jesus is saying about himself by referring to this prophecy?

    b.   Why do you think the chief priests were so upset by his allusion to the son of man in Daniel 7?

8. The Sanhedrin blindfold Jesus and slap him, saying, "Prophesy to us, you Christ. Who is it that struck you?" (Matthew 26:67-68; see also Mark 14:65). They are mocking him for claiming to be a prophet.

    a.   Read the following verses. What does Jesus predict in these passages, and how accurate were his predictions?

        i. **John 13:21-26**

        ii. **Matthew 26:31**

        iii. **Luke 22:34**

b.   Who is the true prophet on this night of Christ's passion?

c.   Read **Isiah 50:6-7.** In light of the background of this prophecy, how might the members of the Sanhedrin unwittingly play a part in fulfilling prophecy even as they mock Jesus for being a prophet?

9.   After Peter denies Jesus three times, the cock crows and "the Lord turned and looked at Peter" (Luke 22:61).

a.   What kind of look do you think Jesus gave Peter at this moment?

b.   Read **Mark 10:21.** How did Jesus look at the rich young man when he walked away from discipleship? How might that shed light on Christ's look at Peter?

c. How would you feel if you were Peter and Jesus looked at you at this moment?

10. Read **Matthew 27:3-4**. Though some translations say Judas "repented," the actual word Matthew uses to describe Judas at this moment means to have remorse or to regret. How do you think Judas' regret is different from full repentance?

D. Application

Reflect

Peter wept bitterly when he realized his sin, and he eventually was reconciled with Jesus. Judas merely felt badly about his actions. Perhaps he was mad at himself, afraid of the consequences, afraid of what others would think of him, discouraged by his weakness, tempted to think he could never change, and tempted to despair thinking he could never be forgiven. Whatever the case, he was more focused on himself than he was on his relationship with Jesus. How do you respond when you sin, when you hurt someone like your spouse or a friend, or when you hurt your relationship with God? In what ways might you be tempted to focus only on yourself in those moments?

Commit

What can you do to be less like Judas when you recognize your faults, weaknesses, and sins? How can you keep your focus on God and the people you may have hurt through what you have done and what you have failed to do? Write down one thing you can do to keep your focus on God and others when you make a mistake, a weakness comes out, or you commit a sin. Then pray to God each day this week for him to help you to do that.

Pray

Read **Psalm 51**, a classic psalm of repentance. It describes King David's heartfelt sorrow for having sinned against God. Choose one line from this psalm that speaks most to you and prayerfully speak those words to God in a way that applies to your life right now.

For more background on this session, see chapters five through nine in Edward Sri's book
No Greater Love: A Biblical Walk Through Christ's Passion.

TALK NOTES

"Are You the Christ?" (Mark 14:61): Jesus' Arrest and Trial Before the Sanhedrin

I. Jesus gives himself over voluntarily; he is in control

    A. "Rise, let us be going; see, my betrayer is at hand" (Mark 14:42)

    B. Jesus knew what was going to happen (see John 18:4)

    C. Jesus is the Good Shepherd who lays down his life for his sheep (see John 10:14-15)

    D. "No one takes [my life] from me, but I lay it down of my own accord" (John 10:18)

    E. By saying "I am he" (John 18:5-6), Jesus is asserting that he is divine

II. Jesus is betrayed by Judas

    A. "Friend, why are you here?" (Matthew 26:50)

    B. "Judas, would you betray the Son of man with a kiss?" (Luke 22:48)

III. The disciples left Jesus (see Mark 14:50)

    A. Recalls Peter and Andrew leaving their nets to follow Jesus (see Mark 1:18)

    B. Recalls James and John "leaving" their father to follow Jesus (see Mark 1:20)

    C. A young man leaves his clothes behind and runs away naked (see Mark 14:51-52)

    D. Implies they have turned away from their discipleship

IV. Jesus before the Sanhedrin

    A. *Gallicantu* (Latin): cock crow

    B. *Sanhedrin* (Greek): council

    C. Sought false testimony against Jesus to condemn him to death (see Matthew 26:59)

    D. "And the high priest stood up …" (Matthew 26:62; see Psalm 27:12; 35:11; 86:14; Wisdom 2:12-20)

    E. "Have you no answer to make?" (Matthew 26:62)

    F. Jesus remains silent (see Matthew 26:63; Isaiah 53:7)

    G. Jesus is put under oath and now must speak (see Matthew 26:63)

    H. "You have said so …" (Matthew 26:64)

    I. Jesus is the Christ, but not in the way that Caiaphas thinks

V. The Son of Man Prophecy (see Matthew 26:64; Daniel 7)

    A. Four beasts represent four Gentile nations

    B. Coming on the clouds symbolizes God's presence

    C. Jesus is claiming to be the divine Son of Man

    D. The chief priests have become the chief beasts

VI. Peter's denial

    A. Peter distances himself physically and spiritually from Christ (see Matthew 26:69-75)

    B. "I do not know what you mean" (Matthew 26:70)

    C. "I do not know the man" (Matthew 26:72, 74)

    D. The cock crows (see Matthew 26:33-35)

    E. "The Lord turned and looked at Peter" (Luke 22:61)

    F. Peter "went out and wept bitterly" (Luke 22:62)

    G. "Simon, son of John, do you love me?" (John 21:16)

        1. *Agape* (Greek): perfect sacrificial love
        2. *Philea* (Greek): imperfect human love

VII. Judas

    A. Judas throws the thirty pieces of silver into the Temple (Matthew 27:5)

    B. Judas did not so much "repent" as he "regretted" what he did (see Matthew 27:3)

    C. Peter repents; he is not focused just on himself

    D. Judas stays focused on himself and his actions

    E. Judas "went [out] and hanged himself" (Matthew 27:5; see Luke 22:62)

NO
GREATER
LOVE

THE TRIAL BEFORE PILATE

Jesus Is Condemned to Death

A. Establish the Context

Though Jesus is arrested, beaten, and condemned to death by the Sanhedrin, we saw how he remains the one in control. When the soldiers and police come to arrest Jesus, he goes out to meet them. He alludes to the divine name, and the crowds draw back and fall to the ground. He is the Good Shepherd who lays down his life for his sheep: "No one takes it from me, I lay it down of my own accord" (John 10:17-18). During his rigged hearing based on false testimony, he remains silent: "He opened not his mouth" (Isaiah 53:7). Only when the high priest Caiaphas puts him under oath does Jesus speak, saying he is "the Son of man seated at the right hand of Power, and coming on the clouds of heaven" (Matthew 26:64)—a claim to be the divine "son of man" from Daniel 7. At this, the Sanhedrin charge him with blasphemy and condemn him to death.

Meanwhile, Peter faced his own trial of sorts outside in the high priest's courtyard as people accuse him of being one of Jesus' disciples. Peter denies Jesus three times, and when Jesus looks at him, he goes out weeping bitterly. Peter will eventually be reconciled with Christ, but Judas' story ends more tragically. In despair, he hangs himself.

Now we turn our attention to how the members of the Sanhedrin carefully plot their next move. They have condemned Jesus to death, but they do not have the authority to carry out capital punishment; they must work with the Roman governor Pontius Pilate and convince him to crucify Jesus.

Pilate quickly recognizes that Jesus is innocent, but when the chief priests keep the pressure on him, Pilate sends Jesus off to be scourged and crowned with thorns, hoping that will placate the Jewish leaders. But when they start threatening Pilate, saying, "If you release this man, you are not Caesar's friend" (John 19:12), it is more pressure than Pilate can bear. He sends the innocent Jesus off to be crucified.

B. Read the Story

Read the following verses that tell of Jesus' arrest and hearing before the Jewish Sanhedrin: **Matthew 27:1-31; Mark 15:1-20; Luke 23:1-25; John 18:28-19:16.**

Read also chapter twelve from *No Greater Love: A Biblical Walk Through Christ's Passion.*

C. Take a Deeper Look

1. **Matthew 27:1** (emphasis added) says, "The chief priests and the elders of the people *took counsel* against Jesus to put him to death."

   a. Read **Psalm 2:2**, which is a messianic psalm foreshadowing the coming of the messiah to Israel. How is the expression "take counsel" used in this verse? How might that foreshadow what the chief priests and elders are doing on Good Friday?

   b. Read the following verses and consider how the Jewish leaders in Jerusalem already have been "taking counsel" against Jesus.

      i. **Matthew 22:15**

      ii. **Matthew 26:3-4**

2. Read **Luke 23:1-4.**

   a. List the accusations the chief priests make against Jesus when they bring him to Pilate:

   b. How are these accusations different from what they charged Jesus with the night before? (Read **Matthew 26:60-66.**)

   c. Why do you think the chief priests "changed their tune" when they brought Jesus to the Roman governor Pontius Pilate?

3. Read **John 18:37-38**. Pilate says to Jesus, "What is truth?"

    a. What does John's Gospel tell us regarding the importance of truth in the following verses?

        i.   **John 1:14**

        ii. **John 1:17**

        iii. **John 5:33**

        iv. **John 8:32**

        v.   **John 14:6**

    b. How is Pilate's view of truth different from what the Gospel of John teaches about truth? What is Pilate ultimately denying when he sarcastically rejects truth?

TAKING ON THE CURSES OF ADAM

"Jesus assumes the thorns that he might cancel the doom; for this cause also was he buried in the earth, that the cursed earth might receive, instead of the curse, the blessing … In [the Garden of] paradise was the fall, and in a Garden was our salvation. From the Tree came sin, and until the Tree [of the Cross] sin lasted; in the evening they sought to hide themselves from the eyes of the Lord and in the evening the robber is brought by the Lord into Paradise."

—St. Cyril of Jerusalem[4]

_____

4   St. Cyril of Jerusalem, P.G. 33, 796A-B. As translated in Jean Danielou, *From Shadows to Reality* (London: Burns & Oates, 1960), 42.

The Expulsion of Adam and Eve from Paradise by Benjamin West

4.   The Scourging and Crowning with Thorns:

   a.   Read **Isaiah 50:6.** What does this prophecy tell us about the suffering Christ would endure?

   b.   The Roman soldiers bend their knees before Jesus and say, "Hail, King!" in jest, ridiculing Jesus for claiming to be a king. Read **Philippians 2:10-11.** What do these verses tell us about how these soldiers might appear before Christ at their own judgment? How do you think they will feel at that moment?

5. Pilate presents the humiliated, scourged, and beaten Jesus to the crowds, saying, "Behold, the man!" (John 19:5, NAB).

    a. What do you think Pilate meant by these words?

    b. Characters in John's Gospel sometimes unconsciously reveal more about Jesus than they intend. Read **John 11:45-53**. How might this be the case in this passage?

    c. Read **Zechariah 6:12-13**.

        i. How do Pilate's words, "Behold, the man" (John 19:5, NAB) echo this prophecy from Zechariah?

        ii. What does this prophecy foretell? What kind of leader does it say will come to Israel?

iii. What, therefore, does Pilate unwittingly reveal about Jesus by presenting him to the people with the words, "Behold, the man…"?

6. At the turning point in Christ's trial before Pilate, the chief priests say, "We have no king but Caesar" (John 19:14-15).

   a. Read **Judges 8:23** and **1 Samuel 8:7**. According to these passages, who is the true king of Israel?

   b. Read **Deuteronomy 17:15**. According to this law, what kind of rulers are prohibited to rule Israelites?

   c. The chief priests are supposed to be the faithful representatives of God's people. What does this background tell us about the chief priests' words, "We have no king but Caesar"?

7. Read **Matthew 27:24**, where Pilate washes his hands to distance himself from the guilt of Christ's innocent blood. Consider how the following passages might shed light on Pilate's action from a biblical perspective:

    a. **Psalm 26:6**

    b. **Deuteronomy 21:1-9** (a passage prescribing certain rituals for when a body is found but the murderer is unknown)

D. Application

Reflect

Pilate tries to ease his conscience by "washing his hands" and attempting to put the responsibility for Christ's death on the Jewish crowds. He says, "I am innocent of this righteous man's blood; see to it yourselves" (Matthew 27:24). Think of a time when you did something wrong and tried to rationalize your sin or blame other people for it. Perhaps it was something a long time ago. Or maybe it is something you are doing right now: the way you treat your spouse, a certain behavior you justify, or something you said to a relative or coworker.

Commit

First, take a moment to prayerfully tell Jesus you do not want to be like Pilate. You do not want to shun responsibility for what you have done. Tell Jesus what you have done and that you are sorry. Then take this sin to Jesus in the sacrament of reconciliation the next time you go to confession. And if your sin has hurt someone else, find a way to tell that person you are sorry if you can.

Pray

An Act of Contrition prayer helps us take full responsibility for our sins, expressing sorrow for how we have offended God and hurt others and asking God for his forgiveness and for his grace to help us avoid sin in the future. If there is a particular Act of Contrition prayer you know and enjoy, pray it now. Here is one version you may consider:

> My God,
> I am sorry for my sins with all my heart.
> In choosing to do wrong
> and failing to do good,
> I have sinned against you
> whom I should love above all things.
> I firmly intend, with your help,
> to do penance,
> to sin no more,
> and to avoid whatever leads me to sin.
> Our Savior Jesus Christ
> suffered and died for us.
> In his name, my God, have mercy.[5]

For more background on this session, see chapters ten through twelve in Edward Sri's book
No Greater Love: A Biblical Walk Through Christ's Passion.

---

[5]   The English translation of the Act of Contrition from *Rite of Penance* © 1974, International Committee on English in the Liturgy, Inc. (ICEL). All rights reserved.

TALK NOTES

The Trial Before Pilate:
Jesus Is Condemned to Death

I. Jesus is led before Pilate

    A. He is led bound (see Mark 15:1)

    B. A large number brings him (see Luke 23:1)

    C. "They began to accuse him" (Luke 23:2)

        1. "Perverting our nation"
        2. "Forbidding us to give tribute to Caesar"
        3. "Saying that he himself is Christ a king"

    D. "Are you the King of the Jews?" (Luke 23:3)

        1. "You have said so"

        2. A qualified affirmative

        3. Jesus is a king, but not as Pilate thinks

        4. "My kingship is not of this world" (John 18:36)

        5. Pilate finds no crime in Jesus (see Luke 23:4)

II. Jesus before Herod

    A. Herod had longed to see and hear Jesus (see Luke 23:8)

    B. He wanted to see a sign, indicating his evil motive (see Luke 11:29)

    C. Unlike Mary who "kept all these things, pondering them in her heart" (Luke 2:19)

III. "What is truth?" (John 18:38)

    A. "If you release this man, you are not Caesar's friend" (John 19:12)

    B. Pilate chooses his own self-interest over the truth

    C. Truth is not an abstract concept; it is a person (see John 14:6)

    D. To reject the truth is to reject Jesus

IV.   Barabbas or Jesus? (see Matthew 27:15-23)

    A. Barabbas was a notorious murderer (see Matthew 27:16; Mark 15:7)

    B. *Bar abba* (Aramaic): son of the father

    C. God calls Israel, "My first-born son" (Exodus 4:22)

V.   Jesus is scourged (see John 19:1)

    A. Lashes in Jewish Law were limited to forty (see Deuteronomy 25:3)

    B. A Roman scourging was far more brutal and had no limitations

VI.   The crowning with thorns (John 19:2)

    A. The soldiers mockingly kneel before him (see Matthew 27:27-29)

    B. All creation will bow before Jesus at the end of time (see Philippians 2:10)

VII.   "Behold, the man" (John 19:5, NAB)

    A. Jesus is the Son of Man from Daniel's vision (see Daniel 7:13-14)

    B. Jesus is the New Adam (see 1 Corinthians 15:45)

    C. Jesus is the King of the Jews (see Zechariah 6:12-13)

VIII.   We have no king but Caesar (John 19:15)

    A. "You are not Caesar's friend" (John 19:12)

    B. Israel was forbidden from making a foreigner their king (see Deuteronomy 17:15)

    C. God alone is king (see Judges 8:23; 1 Samuel 8:4-20)

IX.   Pilate washes his hands

    A. "I am innocent of this righteous man's blood" (Matthew 27:24)

    B. Jesus "suffered under Pontius Pilate" (Apostles' Creed)

NO
GREATER
LOVE

THE DEATH OF THE MESSIAH

Jesus Carries His Cross, Is Crucified, and Dies

A. Establish the Context

The chief priests succeeded in their plans. They pressured Pilate into sending Jesus off to be crucified. Pilate knew Jesus was innocent. He did not buy their accusations of Jesus being a revolutionary king, stirring up the people against Rome. But when the chief priests themselves started stirring up the crowds that day, inciting them to call for Christ's death, Pilate feared a riot might break out. He tried sending Jesus to Herod. He tried having Jesus scourged. He then presents Jesus as a beaten, humiliated, half-dead man, hoping this might appease the blood thirsty crowds. But when the people threaten Pilate saying, "If you release this man, you are not Caesar's friend" (John 19:12), he caves.

Even though he knows the facts of Jesus' innocence, Pilate does not believe in truth. His, "What is truth?" philosophy leaves him with no standard to guide him through this tough situation. So, he does what many people today do when they do not believe in truth—acts in his own self-interest regardless of how it affects others. Pilate defines "his own truth" to protect his reputation and career. Without an objective truth to guide him—a truth that is true for everyone—Pilate sends an innocent man off to be crucified.

In this session, we will walk with Jesus on the way of the Cross. While the Catholic devotion of Stations of the Cross covers several traditional scenes on Christ's journey to Calvary, we will focus on the two that the Gospels explicitly highlight: Simon of Cyrene carrying Jesus' cross, and the women of Jerusalem weeping for Jesus. Next, we will consider what usually happened in Roman crucifixions in general and then unpack the specific events surrounding *Christ's* crucifixion, such as his refusing the initial offer of wine, his clothes being divided, and the three hours of darkness. We will also explore the extraordinary events that occur when Jesus dies, including the Roman centurion's statement, "Truly, this is the Son of God" (Matthew 27:54), the tearing of the temple veil, the unbroken bones of Jesus, the blood and water flowing from his side, and the most unexpected circumstances of his burial.

(Note: The seven last words of Christ from the Cross will be covered in the next session).

ROMAN CRUCIFIXION

Crucifixion did not damage any vital organs, but this was no act of mercy. It was more torturous to die slowly, sometimes over a few days while the weight of the unsupported body gradually would cause the breathing muscles to give out. The person would eventually die of shock or asphyxiation. The fact that Jesus' crucifixion was a shorter one—only six hours (Mark 15:25, 34)—tells us he must have endured a most horrendous scourging. Jesus already may have been on the brink of death by the time he arrived at Calvary.

In Roman crucifixions, the criminal was nailed or bound to the cross with his arms extended and raised. Not being able to move, he was unable to cope with cold, heat, pain, insects, or animals that might bother him. The fact that John's Gospel later tells us about the prints of nails in Jesus' hands indicates that Jesus was not tied to the Cross but nailed to it (see John 20:25; Luke 24:39).

B. Read the Story

Read the following verses that tell of Jesus' carrying his cross to Calvary, his crucifixion, and his death and burial: **Matthew 27:32-66; Mark 15:21-47; Luke 23:26-56; John 19:17-42.**

Read also chapter fourteen from *No Greater Love: A Biblical Walk Through Christ's Passion.*

C. Take a Deeper Look

1. Simon of Cyrene carries the Cross for Jesus.

   a. Read **Luke 23:26**. What does Luke tell us about the way Simon of Cyrene carried Christ's cross?

b. According to what Jesus teaches in the following verses, what must one do to be a disciple?

    i. **Luke 9:23**

    ii. **Luke 14:27**

c. What might this background tell us about Simon of Cyrene?

2. Jesus tells the women of Jerusalem not to weep (Luke 23:28).

a. Read the following passages in which Jesus tells others not to weep. Why does he tell them not to weep?

    i. **Luke 7:11-17**

    ii. **Luke 8:49-55**

b. With this background in mind, why do you think Jesus tells the women of Jerusalem not to weep for him?

3. Psalm 22 is about a righteous man who is being persecuted by his enemies. His experiences prefigure in many ways what Christ endures on Calvary.

    a. Read **Psalm 22:16-18**. What are two or three points made in these three verses that foreshadow what happens to Jesus when he first gets to Calvary?

    b. Read **Psalm 22:7-8**. How do these verses prophetically foreshadow Christ's experience as he is hanging on the Cross?

4. Read **Matthew 27:45**, which tells how from noon until 3 PM, a great darkness covered the earth. Read the following passages from the Old Testament and explain how they each prefigure this darkness on Good Friday.

    a. **Exodus 10:22**

    b. **Amos 8:9-10**

5. John's Gospel presents Jesus' sacrifice on Calvary in light of the Passover sacrifice.

    a. What do the following verses tell us about the Passover?

        i. **Exodus 12:21-23**

        ii. **Exodus 12:46**

        iii. **Numbers 9:9-12**

    b. How do the following verses from Christ's passion remind us of the Passover lamb? (Note that the Passover lambs were slaughtered on the day of preparation before Passover around noon.)

        i. **John 19:14**

        ii. **John 19:29**

        iii. **John 19:32-33**

6. Read **John 19:34**. How was this event foreshadowed by prophets in the following passages?

    a. **Zechariah 12:10**

    b. **Luke 2:33-35**

7. God is sometimes called the God of second chances. One character who appears at Jesus' death is one who got a second chance with Jesus. His name is Nicodemus.

    a. Read **John 3:1**. Who is Nicodemus? How much faith and understanding should we expect from such a man?

    b. Read **John 3:2-10**. What impression do you have of Nicodemus from these verses? How well does he understand Jesus?

    c.   Read **John 7:45-52**. What is your impression of Nicodemus in this scene? Do you think there has been a change in him?

    d.   Read **John 19:39-42** and **John 12:1-5**. Compare Nicodemus' gift with Mary of Bethany's generosity. What does this tell you about Nicodemus' faith and devotion to Jesus?

D. Application

Reflect

St. John Paul II once said that the passion of Christ is *"the culmination of the revelation of God's love."*[6] In 1 Corinthians 13:4-7, St. Paul expounds on the characteristics of authentic love. Love is patient … kind … not jealous or boastful or arrogant or rude … it does not insist on its own way … it is not irritable or resentful … it bears all things … endures all things.

Reflect on the ways in which Jesus, in his passion and death, models these various qualities of love.

---

[6]   St. John Paul II, apostolic letter, *Rosarium Virginis Mariae* (On the Rosary of the Virgin Mary), (October 16, 2002), 22, original emphasis.

Commit

Take a moment to pray and ask God which of these qualities of love you need to grow in the most right now. Consider one concrete area of your life where you can put this into practice this week.

Pray

Ask Jesus to help you imitate him as you strive to live out this aspect of love this week. Then pray the words of St. Paul from **1 Corinthians 13:4-7**, which can be seen as a hymn of love:

"Love is patient and kind;
love is not jealous or boastful;
it is not arrogant or rude.
Love does not insist on its own way;
it is not irritable or resentful;
it does not rejoice at wrong,
but rejoices in the right.
Love bears all things,
believes all things,
hopes all things,
endures all things."

For more background on this session, see chapters thirteen through fifteen in Edward Sri's book *No Greater Love: A Biblical Walk Through Christ's Passion.*

TALK NOTES

The Death of the Messiah:
Jesus Carries His Cross, Is Crucified, and Dies

I. Roman crucifixions

    A. Sent a message: this is what happens when you rebel against Rome

    B. Jesus was likely very near to death when he picked up his cross

II. Simon of Cyrene

    A. Compassion or Compulsion?

        1. Simon carries the Cross "behind Jesus" (See Luke 23:26)

        2. Discipleship involves taking one's cross and following Jesus (see Luke 9:23)

    B. Simon's son, Rufus, may be the same Rufus mentioned by Paul as being "eminent in the Lord" (see Mark 15:21; Romans 16:13)

III. The women of Jerusalem

    A. "*Do not weep* for me, but weep for yourselves and for your children" (Luke 23:28, emphasis added)

        1. The Widow of Nain is told not to weep for her dead son (see Luke 7:13)

        2. A hint that Jesus will be raised from the dead as they were

    B. Jesus uses apocalyptic language to describe the coming destruction of Jerusalem in AD 70 (see Luke 23:29-31)

    C. Jesus is innocent, yet he was crucified. The next generation will be guilty of rebellion, and their punishment will be even more severe (see Luke 23:31)

IV. Crucifixion was designed to prolong death and inflict severe pain

V. The Church of the Holy Sepulchre

    A. Built over the site of Christ's crucifixion, burial, and resurrection

    B. *Calvary* [Latin]: skull

    C. *Golgotha* [Aramaic]: skull (see Matthew 27:33)

    D. Place of death and perhaps the hill was shaped like a skull

TALK NOTES

    E.   Christ crucified was "a stumbling block to the Jews and folly to the Gentiles" (1 Corinthians 1:23)

    F.   In reality, Christ's crucifixion points to the "power of God" (see 1 Corinthians 1:24)

VI.   The Theology of the Cross

    A.   The punishment of an innocent person does not solve the problem of sin

    B.   It is the love of God that saves humanity

    C.   Sin separates us from God

    D.   We do not have the ability to make up for our sins ourselves

    E.   Christ is able to save humanity by his infinite act of love on Calvary, because he is fully divine and fully human

VII.   Wine mixed with myrrh (see Mark 15:23)

    A.   Has narcotic effects (see Proverbs 31:6-7)

    B.   Jesus refuses the drink

        1.   To enter more fully into his passion

        2.   To stay alert and conscious as he continues his ministry from the Cross

VIII.   Jesus' garments are divided (see Matthew 27:35)

    A.   Cast lots for them

    B.   "They have pierced my hands and feet … for my clothing they cast lots" (Psalm 22:16, 18)

    C.   The seamless tunic (see John 19:23-24)

        1.   Same word used for high priest's vestments (see Exodus 28:4; Leviticus 16:4)

        2.   Jesus is the High Priest who is offering his life on the Cross

IX.   The inscription upon the Cross

    A.   INRI – Latin abbreviation for "Jesus of Nazareth, the King of the Jews" (John 19:19)

    B.   Written in Hebrew, Greek, and Latin, signifying the universal scope of Christ's sacrifice (see John 19:20)

X.   Jesus is mocked by three groups (see Matthew 27:39-43)

    A. Those passing by

    B. The chief priests

    C. The criminals crucified with him

    D. Recalls the mockeries in Psalm 22:7-8

    E. "If you are the Son of God …" recalls the devil's words during Christ's three temptations (see Matthew 4:3, 6; 27:40)

XI.   Darkness, veil torn, and earthquake (see Matthew 27:45, 51)

    A. Recalls the three days of darkness in Egypt (see Exodus 10:22)

    B. Recalls the dark day predicted in the prophecy of Amos (see Amos 8:9)

    C. The temple veil is torn (see Mark 15:38)

        1. The sacrificial system has been replaced by Christ's sacrifice

        2. Opens a new level of intimacy with God (see Hebrews 10:19-20)

        3. "Truly this was the Son of God!" (Matthew 27:54)

XII.   Blood and water

    A. Imagery associated with the Church, baptism, and the Eucharist

    B. Eve came from the side of Adam (see Genesis 2:21-22)

    C. The Church is the New Eve born from the side of the New Adam

    D. Jesus is the new Passover Lamb (see John 19:4)

        1. Hyssop branch (see Exodus 12:21-23; John 19:29)

        2. Legs not broken (see Exodus 12:46; John 19:31-37)

NO
GREATER
LOVE

THE SEVEN LAST WORDS

Jesus the Teacher at Calvary

A. Establish the Context

In the previous session, we walked with Jesus on his way to Calvary. Simon of Cyrene's brief encounter with Jesus transforms him. He picks up the Cross and follows Jesus, giving a visual image of discipleship. Jesus also comforts the women of Jerusalem, encouraging them to weep not for him but for their children, who will suffer even more than he when Jerusalem eventually rebels against Rome.

At Calvary, we saw Jesus refusing the wine mixed with myrrh, desiring not to have his pain deadened, but to drink fully from the cup of his suffering. We also considered the deeper significance of many small details mentioned in the Gospel accounts of Christ's crucifixion. These include: the inscription on the Cross: "This Is Jesus, the King of the Jews" (Matthew 27:37) intended to mock Christ that actually reveals the truth that Jesus is the King of all nations; his clothes divided symbolizing division of the human family while the seamless tunic woven "from top to bottom" represents Church unity; Jesus' unbroken bones pointing to him as the Passover Lamb; and the blood and water from Christ's side pointing to baptism and the Eucharist.

Now we turn our attention to what is commonly known as Christ's "Seven Last Words," which refers to the seven brief sayings Jesus uttered from the Cross before he died. For centuries, these words have been the subject of many sermons, books, devotions, and musical pieces. Think of these seven last words not merely as words spoken to the world in general, but as personal words spoken to you. Before Jesus died, he was thinking of you and what you would be going through this year, this month, this day. He wants to give you a certain message to encourage you, comfort you, or challenge you. As St. Augustine once observed, "The tree upon which were fixed the members of Him dying was even the chair of the Master teaching."[7]

B. Read the Story

Read the following verses that represent the seven last sayings of Jesus from the Cross:

Luke 23:34

Luke 23:43

John 19:26-27

Matthew 27:46

John 19:28

John 19:30

Luke 23:46

Read also chapter seventeen from *No Greater Love: A Biblical Walk Through Christ's Passion.*

C. Take a Deeper Look

1. Read **Luke 23:34.**

    a. What are the first of the last words of Christ?

    b. What did Jesus teach in the following verses?

        i. **Matthew 5:7**

---

[7] As quoted in St. Thomas Aquinas, *Summa Theologica*, III.46.4.

    ii. **Matthew 5:43-45**

    iii. **Luke 11:4**

    iv. **Matthew 18:21-23**

  c. How might these other teachings of Jesus relate to what Jesus says from the Cross in **Luke 23:34**?

2. Read **Luke 23:43**.

  a. What are the second of the last words of Christ?

  b. Read **Luke 23:42**. What did the good thief ask from Jesus?

c. Read **Luke 23:43**. What did Jesus offer him? Was this what the good thief asked for, or something more, or something less?

3. Read **John 19:26-27**.

    a. What are the third of the last words of Christ?

    b. Read the following verses. What do they each tell us about the beloved disciple?

        i. **John 13:25**

        ii. **John 19:26**

        iii. **John 20:8**

        iv. **John 21:7**

        v. **John 21:24**

c. Some saints and scholars have seen the beloved disciple not only as an individual disciple, but the model disciple—one who represents all faithful disciples. How might the overall picture of the beloved disciple in John's Gospel support this interpretation?

d. If the beloved disciple represents all faithful disciples, what does it mean for us that Jesus says to him, "Behold, your mother!" (John 19:27)?

4. Read **Matthew 27:46.**

a. What are the fourth of the last words of Christ?

b. In these words, Jesus is quoting from Psalm 22. Consider the background of this Psalm.

    i. Read **Psalm 22:1-2**. How does this shed light on what Jesus was facing on Good Friday?

    ii. Read **Psalm 22:3-4** and **Psalm 22:9-11**. Do these verses sound like a man in despair or a man with hope even in distress? Explain.

    iii. Read **Psalm 22:23-28**. How does the man in this psalm conclude with great confidence that God will come to rescue him from his afflictions?

    iv. What might this background tell us about what Jesus meant by quoting from Psalm 22?

5. Read **John 19:28.**

    a.   What are the fifth of the last words of Christ?

    b.   Read the following Old Testament passages and explain how they foreshadow Christ's thirst on the Cross.

        i.   **Psalm 69:21**

        ii.   **Psalm 22:15**

"I THIRST"
(John 19:28)

"Just put yourself in front of the tabernacle. Don't let anything disturb you. Hear your own name and 'I Thirst.' I thirst for purity, I thirst for poverty, I thirst for obedience, I thirst for that wholehearted love, I thirst for that total surrender. Are we living a deeply contemplative life? He thirsts for that total surrender."

– St. Teresa of Calcutta (Mother Teresa)[8]

8   St. Teresa of Calcutta (Mother Teresa), *Where There Is Love, There Is God* (New York: Doubleday, 2010), 52.

    c.   Read **John 4:7.** Here we see Jesus expressed his thirst once before. But as the *Catechism of the Catholic Church* explains, he thirsts for more than water; he thirsts for us: "Jesus thirsts; his asking arises from the depths of God's desire for us. Whether we realize it or not, prayer is the encounter of God's thirst with ours. God thirsts that we may thirst for him" (CCC 2560). How does this view of Jesus' "thirst" change the way you look at prayer?

6.   Read **John 19:30.**

    a.   What are the sixth of the last words of Christ?

    b.   Read the following verses and explain what Jesus says he is bringing to completion:

        i.   **John 4:34**

        ii.   **John 17:4**

    c.   With this background in mind, what do you think Jesus means when he says from the Cross, "It is finished"?

7. Read **Luke 23:46.**

    a.   What are the seventh of the last words of Christ?

    b.   Read **Luke 9:44.** Into whose hands did Jesus predict he would be handed over?

    c.   Read **Luke 23:46.** Ultimately, into whose hands does Jesus entrust his spirit?

    d.   Read the following verses and explain what they tell us about the Father's *hands*:

        i. **John 10:27-29**

        ii. **Acts 4:26-28**

        iii. **Acts 4:29-30**

e. What does this background tell us about the confidence Jesus must have had in entrusting his spirit into his Father's hands?

D. Application

Reflect

Which of the seven of the last words of Christ speaks to you most personally? Perhaps one of them comforts you, encourages you, or challenges you in a particular way. Take a few moments to prayerfully ask God which of these last words you need to hear the most right now, and why.

Commit

Make a commitment to bring these words to mind each day for the next week. Commit these particular words of Christ to memory. Write them down in a journal. Write them on a sheet of paper you put in your Bible or on your refrigerator, or tape them on your bathroom mirror so you see them first thing in the morning. Say them before you do your daily prayer.

Pray

Take a moment right now to prayerfully imagine Jesus speaking these words to you. Imagine yourself at Calvary on Good Friday and no one else is around. It is just you and Jesus. He is approaching his dying moments. Imagine him opening his eyes and looking straight at you and saying these particular words personally to you. How would you feel at that moment? What would you be thinking? What particularly do you think Jesus means when he speaks these words to *you*? How do they apply to your life? What might Jesus be asking of you or hoping for you with these words?

Then, ask God to help you to not only remember these words each day, but to live the message of these words—to apply them to your daily life.

For more background on this session, see chapters sixteen through twenty-two in Edward Sri's book
No Greater Love: A Biblical Walk Through Christ's Passion.

TALK NOTES

The Seven Last Words:
Jesus the Teacher at Calvary

I. "My God, my God, why have you forsaken me?" (Matthew 27:46)

    A. Was Jesus abandoned by his Father?

    B. Quoting first verse of Psalm 22 recalls the entire psalm and Jesus' ultimate deliverance *Psalm 27 & 28*

II. The seven last words

    A. "Father, forgive them; for they know not what they do" (Luke 23:34)

    B. "Today you will be with me in Paradise" (Luke 23:43)

    C. "Behold, your son … Behold, your mother" (John 19:26-27)

    D. "My God, my God, why have you forsaken me?" (Matthew 27:46)

    E. "I thirst" (John 19:28)

    F. "It is finished" (John 19:30)

    G. "Father, into your hands I commit my spirit!" (Luke 23:46)

III. "Father, forgive them; for they know not what they do" (Luke 23:34)

    A. "Love your enemies, do good to those who hate you, bless those who curse you, pray for those who abuse you" (Luke 6:27-28)

    B. We need the help of the Holy Spirit to forgive others (see CCC 2843)

IV. "Today you will be with me in Paradise" (Luke 23:43)

    A. He literally "was saying" these words, repeating them like a prayer

    B. The good thief moments before had mocked Jesus (see Matthew 27:44)

    C. He becomes a model of repentance

the Good thief

        1. He rebuked the other criminal as Jesus rebuked the evil spirits (see Luke 4:35, 39, 41; 23:40) *(Satan)*

        2. He admits his guilt (see Luke 23:41)

        3. He trusts in the mercy of Jesus (see Luke 23:43)

Fr Josh Johnson   Ask Father Josh Podcast

on this day you will be w/me in paradise

V.   "Behold, your son … Behold, your mother" (John 19:26-27)

[handwritten: son]

[handwritten margin note: John represents the (us) faithful disciples]

    A. Places Mary into the care of the beloved disciple

    B. The beloved disciple represents all faithful disciples who receive Mary as mother

VI.   "I thirst" (John 19:28)

    A. Recalls Psalm 22:15 and Psalm 69:21

    B. St. Teresa of Calcutta taught us to picture Jesus saying this to us personally

VII.   "It is finished" (John 19:30)

    A. The fulfillment of God's plans

    B. Jesus is finishing the work of the Father (see John 4:34; 17:4)

    C. The hour has arrived for the devil to be defeated (see John 2:4; 12:23, 31-32)

    D. Jesus offered himself at the Last Supper, and now that offering is brought to completion on the Cross

VIII.   "Father, into your hands I commit my spirit!" (Luke 23:46)

    A. A quotation from Psalm 31:5

    B. Jesus is actively surrendering his life to the Father

IX.   The Passion

    A. The Latin root of "passion" refers to suffering

    B. It also indicates the passionate love Jesus has for us

    C. "God is love" (1 John 4:8)

    D. Every Mass is a pilgrimage to Calvary

NO GREATER LOVE

A BIBLICAL WALK THROUGH
CHRIST'S PASSION

RESPONSES TO THE STUDY QUESTIONS

How to Use These Responses

After completing the home preparation, discussing the questions, and viewing the video presentation, the final step is to review the responses to the questions. These responses summarize the main points from the session and help you continue your Bible study in the next session.

Although it can be tempting to read these responses ahead of time, please wait until after you have completed the questions for each session and engaged in the small-group discussion. It is not necessary to have the "right" answers before going to the small-group discussion. In fact, one purpose of the discussion is for participants to learn by sharing their insights and questions with each other and, through that discussion, coming to a better understanding of the Scripture passage. This makes for a better Bible study experience for everyone.

For best results, follow these steps in order:

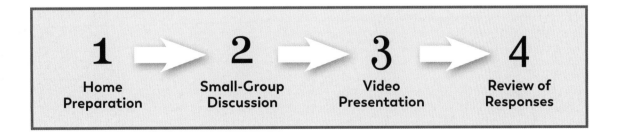

1	→	2	→	3	→	4
Home Preparation		Small-Group Discussion		Video Presentation		Review of Responses

NO
GREATER
LOVE

THE PRAYER OF THE AGONY
Jesus in Gethsemane

A. Establish the Context

Facilitators: If you like, have someone read aloud the "Establish the Context" section.

B. Read the Story

Facilitators: Explain to the participants that the listed verses are their readings for the following session. No prior reading is needed for this session. Begin your small-group discussion with a brief prayer.

C. Take a Deeper Look

Facilitators: Have the participants respond to these questions and invite them to share their responses with the group

1. *What inspires you most about Jesus' prayer in Gethsemane: "My Father, if it be possible, let this chalice pass from me; nevertheless, not as I will, but as you will" (Matthew 26:39)?*

   Answers will vary: Some may be moved by Jesus' humanity in this prayer—that he felt repulsed by, as any human would, the thought of the pain and suffering he was about to endure. Others might comment on how grateful they are that Jesus still said "yes" and embraced his passion and death for us. Others might be inspired by Jesus' will being perfectly united with the Father's even though it will cause him much pain.

2. *What do you think it means to do the Father's will and not your own? How does this prayer inspire you to do God's will more in your life?*

   God's plan is always better than anything we can come up with on our own. We may have certain desires, goals, hopes, and expectations in life, but God invites us to place everything in his hands, trusting that his plan leads to what is best for us. Consider the following verse from Scripture about how the Father has a plan for each of our lives: "For I know the plans I have for you, says the LORD. Plans for welfare and not for evil, to give you a future and a hope" (Jeremiah 29:11). The Father's will—his plan for our lives—is for our happiness. It is for our "welfare" and to give us "a future and a hope" in life. Jesus models for us perfect trust and surrender to the Father's plan.

D. Application

Facilitators: If time allows, invite group members to share their responses from this session's application questions.

After sharing your responses in the small group, watch Edward Sri's video presentation on *Session One – The Prayer of the Agony: Jesus in Gethsemane.*

Judas Betrays Jesus With a Kiss (Fresco in the Collegiata of San Gimignana, Italy)

"ARE YOU THE CHRIST?"
(Mark 14:61)

Jesus' Arrest and Trial Before the Sanhedrin

Facilitators: Read these responses to the questions ahead of time to help you prepare to lead the small-group discussion.

Participants: Reinforce what you have learned by reviewing these responses after your small-group discussion and before you continue to the next session.

A. Establish the Context

Facilitators: Take a moment to establish the context and what was learned in the previous session.

B. Read the Story

Facilitators: Ask someone to summarize the readings for this session. Begin your small-group discussion with a brief prayer.

C. Take a Deeper Look

Facilitators: If there is time, have someone read each passage aloud before it is discussed.

1. *Read **Mark 14:42** and **John 18:1-6.***

   a. *Does Jesus seem to be taken by surprise by Judas and those coming to arrest him? Who seems to be in charge in this scene of his arrest?*

   Jesus is not caught by surprise. He knows all that is about to happen. At the end of his prayer in Gethsemane, he says to his disciples, "Rise, let us be going; see, my betrayer is at hand" (Mark 14:42). When the arrest party arrives, Jesus knew all that was to befall him (see John 18:4). He takes the initiative and goes forward to meet them (see John 18:4). He asks, "Whom do you seek?" (John 18:4). This does not look like someone trying to flee. When he identifies himself, the soldiers and temple guards all draw back a few steps and fall to the ground (see John 18:6). A glimpse of Jesus' full power is revealed. As the soldiers and officers seem in a daze, Jesus has to take charge of the situation. He is the one who moves along the process of his arrest, asking a second time, "Whom do you seek?" (John 18:7). He once again identifies himself, clearly not trying to hide or veil his identity. And he commands the arrest party to let his disciples go (see John 18:8). Notice how Jesus is the one in charge. He is the one taking the initiative. He is the one doing all the questioning.

   b. *Read **John 10:14-15, 17-18.** What might this tell us about the role Jesus will play when he is arrested and eventually crucified?*

   In John 10:14-15, Jesus describes himself as the Good Shepherd who lays down his life for his sheep. In John 10:17-18, he said, "I lay down my life, that I may take it again. No one takes it from me, but I lay it down of my own accord." Here in Gethsemane during Christ's arrest—and throughout his passion—others will take Jesus away, beat him, scourge him, and crucify him. But we must see that Jesus is the one freely choosing to be arrested and handed over to the chief priests, just as he is the one who will allow the Roman soldiers to scourge him, mock him, and crucify him. No one takes his life from him. He is the one in control of the events unfolding before him.

2. *When the crowd comes to the garden looking for Jesus of Nazareth, Jesus responds, "I am he" (John 18:5), and they "drew back and fell to the ground" (John 18:4-6). Consider how this scene reveals a glimpse of Jesus' divine power.*

a. *Read **Exodus 3:14**. How is the expression "I AM" used in this passage with Moses at the burning bush? And what might this tell us about Jesus' similar expression in Gethsemane, "I am he"?*

God reveals his divine name to Moses at the burning bush: "I AM WHO I AM" (Exodus 3:14). When Jesus says, "I am he" (*ego eimi* in Greek), the expression could simply mean he is identifying himself as the one the soldiers and police are seeking. But in John's Gospel, the expression carries much more weight. The words can also recall the divine name revealed to Moses. That is how it is used in John 8:58, where Jesus says, "Before Abraham was, I am" and the Jewish leaders want to stone him to death for associating himself with the divine name. Finally, upon hearing Jesus say, "I am he," the soldiers and police in Gethsemane draw back and fall to the ground, further showing the supernatural power of these words.

b. *Read **Psalm 35:4** and **Psalm 56:9**. What might these verses tell us about the crowd turning back when they came to arrest Jesus?*

Both psalms feature a righteous man who is being persecuted by his enemies. In Psalm 35, the psalmist prays that those who seek his life will be "turned back" and confounded. In Psalm 56, the man prays that his enemies be "turned back." That John's Gospel uses the same word to describe the soldiers and police "withdrawing" shows that they are in the role of the wicked enemies of these psalmists, the ones persecuting the righteous man, who is Jesus. The enemies of Christ are turned back and confounded just as described in the psalms.

c. *Read **Revelation 1:12-17**. Why does St. John fall to the ground? What might that tell us about the crowd falling down when they come to arrest Jesus in Gethsemane?*

In the book of Revelation, St. John sees Jesus, the Son of Man, in glory. Several apocalyptic images describe his glory and power; for example, he appears with eyes like a flame of fire holding seven stars and his face shining like the sun. Seeing this, St. John falls on his feet as though dead in fear and awe and worship before the divine Son of Man. The fact that the crowd in Gethsemane falls to the ground in a similar way indicates that, at least for a moment, they are overpowered by some experience of Christ's glory like St. John was in the book of Revelation.

3. *A new Isaac:*

    a. *Read **Genesis 22:1-18**. In what ways does this scene prefigure Jesus' last week of his life when he enters Jerusalem?*

	What happens to Abraham and Isaac in these verses from Genesis 22?	How might Abraham and Isaac prefigure what happens to Jesus in his last week in Jerusalem?
Genesis 22:2 *and **John 3:16***	God asks Abraham to take his "only begotten son" (Genesis 22:2), whom he loves, to offer him as a burnt offering on a mountain in Moriah. (It is interesting that a burnt offering is an offering for sin and Moriah later becomes known as Jerusalem.)	God offers Jesus, his "only-begotten son" (John 3:16), as a sacrifice on a mountain in Jerusalem. (Like the sacrifice of Isaac, Jesus' sacrifice is an offering for sin. And he's sacrificed on the same Mount Moriah, which becomes known as Jerusalem.)
Genesis 22:3 *and **Matthew 21:1-9***	Abraham and Isaac travel to Moriah on a donkey.	Jesus will enter Jerusalem on a donkey (see Matthew 21:1-9).
Genesis 22:6 *and **John 19:17***	Abraham laid the wood for the sacrifice on Isaac, who carried it up the mountain.	Jesus will carry the wood of the Cross to Calvary.
Genesis 22:9 *and **John 19:18**; **Acts 5:30***	Isaac was bound and laid on the wood for the sacrifice.	Jesus was nailed to the Cross, the wood for his sacrifice

b. *Notice how Matthew's account of Jesus in the garden of Gethsemane recalls what happened to Isaac on Mount Moriah:*

	Isaac on Mount Moriah (Genesis 22)	Jesus on Mount of Olives (Matthew 26)
Read **Genesis 22:5** and **Matthew 26:36**	*What does Abraham say to his men?* **"Stay here … I and the lad will go yonder and worship."**	*What does Jesus say to his disciples?* **"Sit here, while I go yonder and pray."**
Read **Genesis 22:6** and **Matthew 26:47**	*What does Abraham take for the sacrifice?* **"knife (*machaira*) and wood (*zula*)"**	*What do the men coming to arrest Jesus bring with them?* **"swords (*machariōn*) and clubs (*zulōn*)"** (Note to leader: the words in Greek for "swords" and "clubs" are the same words used in Genesis 22 for "knife" and "wood")
Read **Genesis 22:10** and **Matthew 26:51**	*What does Abraham do with his hand?* Abraham **"put forth his hand, and took the knife."**	*What does one of the disciples do with his hand?* He **"stretched out his hand and drew his sword."**
Read **Genesis 22:12** and **Matthew 26:50**	*What does the angel tell Abraham not to do with the boy?* **"Do not lay your hand on the boy"**	*What does the crowd do with Jesus?* The crowd **"laid hands"** on Christ.

4. *Matthew 26:62 notes that the high priest "stood up."*

    a. *Read the following verses. What do they tell us about those who have "risen" or "stood up" against the righteous?*

        i. ***Psalm 27:12***
        "False witnesses have risen against me."

        ii. ***Psalm 35:11***
        "Malicious witnesses rise up."

        iii. ***Psalm 86:14***
        "Insolent men have risen up against me ... ruthless men seek my life."

    b. *What might this background tell us about the high priest who "stood up" during Christ's trial, pressing him to answer?*

    The high priest stands up against Christ, like the wicked in the Old Testament who stood up against God's faithful ones. The chief priests sought false witnesses, just as the wicked do in Psalm 27:12 and Psalm 35:11. They rise up and seek Christ's life as the wicked in Psalm 86:14 do.

5. *Read **Matthew 26:63** and **Isaiah 53:7**. What does this prophecy from Isaiah tell us about Jesus' silence before Caiaphas?*

Isaiah 53 is known as the "Suffering Servant" song. It is a prophecy about God's faithful servant who will bear our griefs and carry our sorrows and be "wounded for our transgressions" and "bruised for our iniquities" (Isaiah 53:4-5). He "makes himself an offering for sin" (Isaiah 53:10). "He was oppressed, and he was afflicted, yet he opened not his mouth; like a lamb that is led to the slaughter ... so he opened not his mouth" (Isaiah 53:7). Jesus remains silent up to this point in his trial, not answering the false charges against him, fulfilling this prophecy of Isaiah. This means Jesus is the suffering servant, the lamb led to the slaughter, the one who is wounded for our transgressions and makes himself an offering for sin—just as Isaiah had foretold.

6. *Caiaphas says to Jesus, "I adjure you, by the living God, tell us if you are the Christ" (Matthew 26:63). Read **1 Kings 22:14-16** about a conversation between the king and the prophet Micaiah.*

    a. *When the king uses the language "I adjure you" in this passage, what is he wanting from Micaiah?*

    The king uses the expression "I adjure you" in the context of commanding Micaiah to speak nothing but the truth: "I adjure you that you speak to me nothing but the truth in the name of the LORD" (1 Kings 22:16).

b. *When Micaiah uses the expression, "As the LORD lives," what is he emphasizing?*

Micaiah is emphasizing that he is telling the truth—that he is communicating to the king what God has spoken to him. "As the LORD lives, what the LORD says to me, that I will speak" (1 Kings 22:14).

c. *And how might this shed light on why Jesus finally answers the high priest?*

The high priest is pressuring Jesus to answer. He uses this strong, technical language from the Jewish biblical tradition to command someone to speak and to speak the truth. This language "as the LORD lives" and "I adjure you" is formal courtroom language, putting someone under oath. Jesus is being put under oath and is being commanded by the high priest with the strongest possible language to speak. Put under this oath, Jesus will finally speak.

7. *Jesus refers to himself as "the Son of man seated at the right hand of Power, and coming on the clouds of heaven" (Matthew 26:64). This is an allusion to the famous "son of man" prophecy in Daniel. Read **Daniel 7:13-14**.*

a. *What do you think Jesus is saying about himself by referring to this prophecy?*

Jesus is claiming to be the son of man of Daniel 7—the one who comes on the clouds of heaven and is given an everlasting dominion over all nations.

b. *Why do you think the chief priests were so upset by his allusion to the son of man in Daniel 7?*

Jesus describes himself in ways that put himself on par with God. He describes himself as being "seated at the right hand of Power"—an image of him sitting on a throne at the right hand of God.

He also refers to himself as the son of man of Daniel 7, who was coming on the clouds of heaven. In Scripture, the cloud symbolizes God's holy presence, descending on Mount Sinai, guiding the Israelites through the desert, overshadowing the tabernacle, and filling the Holy of Holies in the Temple. For Jesus to describe himself as coming on the clouds of heaven, he is associating himself with the divine presence and claiming to do something only God can do. This is the main reason the Sanhedrin charge Jesus with blasphemy.

8. *The Sanhedrin blindfold Jesus and slap him, saying, "Prophesy to us, you Christ. Who is it that struck you?" (Matthew 26:67-68; see also Mark 14:65). They are mocking him for claiming to be a prophet.*

    a. *Read the following verses. What does Jesus predict in these passages, and how accurate were his predictions?*

        i. *John 13:21-26*
        Judas will betray Jesus.

        ii. *Matthew 26:31*
        The disciples will fall away this night.

        iii. *Luke 22:34*
        Peter will deny Jesus three times before the cock crows.

All of Jesus' predictions take place.

    b. *Who is the true prophet on this night of Christ's passion?*

Jesus is the true prophet. He accurately predicted Judas' betrayal, Peter's three denials, and the disciples falling away and scattering.

    c. *Read **Isaiah 50:6-7**. In light of the background of this prophecy, how might the members of the Sanhedrin unwittingly play a part in fulfilling prophecy even as they mock Jesus for being a prophet?*

The prophecy in Isaiah foretells how Christ will give his back to smites in his scourging and not hide his face from shame and spitting during his trial before the Sanhedrin. The irony is that while the chief priests spit at Christ, slap his face, and mock him for being a prophet, their violent and mocking acts fulfill what Isaiah foretold. In their actions that mock Jesus as a prophet, they unwittingly reveal him to be the one fulfilling prophecy.

9. *After Peter denies Jesus three times, the cock crows and "the Lord turned and looked at Peter" (Luke 22:61).*

    a. *What kind of look do you think Jesus gave Peter at this moment?*

Answers will vary. Some might say they envision a stern look. Others might say a look of disappointment or sorrow. Some might say a look of gentleness, mercy, and love.

b. *Read **Mark 10:21**. How did Jesus look at the rich young man when he walked away from discipleship? How might that shed light on Christ's look at Peter?*

Jesus looked at the rich young man with love, even though the man was turning down discipleship with Jesus. That is likely what Jesus is doing with Peter: looking at him with love—with compassion and sorrow for how Peter must be feeling. Jesus surely is sorrowful that his chief apostle has failed so miserably, and yet, he still looks at Peter with love. He still loves Peter. This reminds us that no matter what we have done, we are still beloved in Christ's eyes. He certainly points out our sins and calls us to repent, but that does not take away from how steadfast his love for us remains, even when we have been unfaithful to him.

c. *How would you feel if you were Peter and Jesus looked at you at this moment?*

Answers will vary.

10. *Read **Matthew 27:3-4**. Though some translations say Judas "repented," the actual word Matthew uses to describe Judas at this moment means to have remorse or to regret. How do you think Judas' regret is different from full repentance?*

Judas acknowledges his sin, saying, "I have sinned." He acknowledges Jesus is innocent and the harm he has done to Jesus: "I have sinned against innocent blood." He even throws the bribe money back to the chief priests as a way to dissociate himself from anything he gained from his treacherous act. He clearly feels badly about what he did. But the word Matthew's Gospel uses to describe Judas at this moment means to regret or to have changed with remorse. This is a good first step toward repentance but is not enough. To repent means to turn around or turn away from sin and turn toward God. It's a fundamental change in direction in one's life. Judas might regret his sin, but that doesn't mean he has turned to God and asked forgiveness and recommitted his life to God's ways. We might regret our actions for many reasons that fall short of repentance: We are afraid of what others will think of us. We are afraid of the consequences. We are upset about what this means for us. We are upset we put ourselves in this situation. We are upset that we are so weak and not as holy as we think we should be. Regret is focused on self. Repentance is focused on God and our relationship with him.

D. Application

Facilitators: If time allows, invite group members to share their responses from this session's application questions.

After sharing your responses in the small group, watch Edward Sri's video presentation on
Session Two – "Are You the Christ?" (Mark 14:61): Jesus' Arrest and Trial Before the Sanhedrin.

NO
GREATER
LOVE

THE TRIAL BEFORE PILATE
Jesus Is Condemned to Death

Facilitators: Read these responses to the questions ahead of time to help you prepare to lead the small-group discussion.

Participants: Reinforce what you have learned by reviewing these responses after your small-group discussion and before you continue to the next session.

A. Establish the Context
Facilitators: Take a moment to establish the context and what was learned in the previous session.

B. Read the Story
Facilitators: Ask someone to summarize the readings for this session. Begin your small-group discussion with a brief prayer.

C. Take a Deeper Look
Facilitators: If there is time, have someone read each passage aloud before it is discussed.

1. **Matthew 27:1** *(emphasis added) says, "The chief priests and the elders of the people* took counsel *against Jesus to put him to death."*

   a. *Read **Psalm 2:2**, which is a messianic psalm foreshadowing the coming of the messiah to Israel. How is the expression "take counsel" used in this verse? How might that foreshadow what the chief priests and elders are doing on Good Friday?*

   "The rulers take counsel against the Lord and his anointed." This is about how the anointed king is being plotted against, and it is a foreshadowing of how the rulers of this world will conspire against the messiah (the word messiah means "anointed one").

   Matthew's Gospel notes how these members of the Sanhedrin "take counsel" against Jesus to recall this prophetic foreshadowing from Psalm 2. The chief priests and elders are the wicked rulers who conspire against the Lord and his Anointed One, the Messiah, Jesus Christ. All that is happening to Christ on this day was foreshadowed in the Old Testament.

   b. *Read the following verses and consider how the Jewish leaders in Jerusalem already have been "taking counsel" against Jesus.*

      i. **Matthew 22:15**
         The Pharisees "took counsel" against Jesus, trying to entangle him in his talk.

      ii. **Matthew 26:3-4**
         The chief priests and elders gathered at Caiaphas' house and "took counsel" about how to arrest Jesus by stealth.

2. *Read **Luke 23:1-4.***

   a. *List the accusations the chief priests make against Jesus when they bring him to Pilate:*

      • They accuse Jesus of "perverting" (or "leading astray") the people.
      • They accuse Jesus of not allowing people to pay taxes to Caesar.
      • They accuse Jesus of claiming to be a king, the messiah.
      • They accuse Jesus of "stirring up the people" throughout Galilee, Judea, and Jerusalem.

   b. *How are these accusations different from what they charged Jesus with the night before? (Read **Matthew 26:60-66**.)*

   Before the Sanhedrin, Jesus was accused of saying he would destroy the Temple. He was also charged with blasphemy for having claimed to be the "son of man" from Daniel 7.

c. *Why do you think the chief priests "changed their tune" when they brought Jesus to the Roman governor Pontius Pilate?*

Pilate would not be concerned about religious matters regarding the Temple, blasphemy, and who the "son of man" is in the prophecy of Daniel 7. Pilate's main concern is maintaining Roman order. This is why the chief priests present Jesus to Pilate in ways that might grab the attention of the Roman governor. They paint a picture of Jesus as someone causing unrest and undermining the people's loyalty to Rome and thus, a threat to the Empire. They make Jesus out to be a revolutionary messiah.

3. *Read **John 18:37-38**. Pilate says to Jesus, "What is truth?"*

a. *What does John's Gospel tell us regarding the importance of truth in the following verses?*

   i. ***John 1:14***
   'The Word [the Son of God] became flesh and dwelt among us, full of grace and truth."

   ii. ***John 1:17***
   "Grace and truth came through Jesus Christ."

   iii. ***John 5:33***
   John the Baptist "has borne witness to the truth."

   iv. ***John 8:32***
   "The truth will make you free."

   v. ***John 14:6***
   Jesus says, "I am the way, and the truth, and the life." (Jesus himself is truth!)

b. *How is Pilate's view of truth different from what the Gospel of John teaches about truth? What is Pilate ultimately denying when he sarcastically rejects truth?*

The Gospel of John makes clear that the Son of God, who is called "The Word," became man in Jesus Christ in order to reveal the fullness of truth. Jesus is full of truth (see John 1:14). Truth comes through Jesus (see John 1:17). Other prophets, like John the Baptist, bore witness to Jesus as the Truth (see John 5:33). This truth is liberating; it leads to authentic freedom (see John 8:32). And that truth is found in Jesus who is the Truth (see John 14:6).

Pilate, however, rejects all this. He does not see the truth that will set him free. For Pilate, truth—a real objective truth, the truth about human life, the truth about God, a truth that is true for everyone—is not important. According to him, everyone can make up "their own truth." That's what Pilate himself does on Good Friday. He knows the facts: he knows Jesus is not a threat to the Roman Empire, and he knows Jesus is innocent, but those facts do not matter. What matters is that he protects his reputation and career and his own self-interest. That is "his truth." So, as a result of his relativism—his "what is truth?" philosophy—Pilate sends an innocent man off to be crucified.

4. *The Scourging and Crowning with Thorns:*

   a. *Read **Isaiah 50:6**. What does this prophecy tell us about the suffering Christ would endure?*

   "I gave my back to those who struck me, and my cheeks to those who pulled out the beard; I hid not my face from shame and spitting."

   This prophecy tells of Christ's scourging: his being mocked and spit at by the chief priests and mocked and struck by the Roman soldiers when they crowned him with thorns.

   b. *The Roman soldiers bend their knees before Jesus and say, "Hail, King!" in jest, ridiculing Jesus for claiming to be a king. Read **Philippians 2:10-11**. What do these verses tell us about how these soldiers might appear before Christ at their own judgment? How do you think they will feel at that moment?*

   St. Paul says that "at the name of Jesus every knee should bow, in heaven and on earth and under the earth" (Philippians 2:10). On Good Friday, they kneel before Jesus in jest. But at their judgment day, they will find themselves in the same position, having to bend their knees before Jesus the Lord and Judge of all. And at that moment, they will probably greatly regret what they did on Good Friday.

5. *Pilate presents the humiliated, scourged, and beaten Jesus to the crowds, saying, "Behold, the man!" (John 19:5, NAB).*

   a. *What do you think Pilate meant by these words?*

   Answers will vary.

   b. *Characters in John's Gospel sometimes unconsciously reveal more about Jesus than they intend. Read **John 11:45-53**. How might this be the case in this passage?*

   Here, the high priest Caiaphas was responding to his colleagues' fears that Jesus might gain such widespread popularity that the Romans will be threatened by the growing movement and want to destroy the Temple and the people before it gets out of control. Caiaphas says, "It is expedient for you that one man should die for the people, and that the whole nation should not perish." Caiaphas meant this in the sense that it is better that one man, Jesus, be killed than that the Romans should crush the whole nation of Israel. But John's Gospel sees a lot more in these words and points it out for us. Caiaphas unwittingly is giving a prophecy about how it is better for one man, Jesus, to die for our sins, so that the whole nation, indeed, all the children of God, could be saved and gathered into one.

c. *Read **Zechariah 6:12-13**.*

    i. *How do Pilate's words, "Behold, the man" (John 19:5, NAB) echo this prophecy from Zechariah?*

    Zechariah's prophecy contains these same words, "Behold, the man…"

    ii. *What does this prophecy foretell? What kind of leader does it say will come to Israel?*

    The prophecy tells of a future king, a son of David, who "shall bear royal honor" and "sit and rule upon his throne." The prophecy describes this future king as "the Branch"—which is an allusion to other Old Testament prophecies about a royal branch coming out of the stump of Jesse, David's father (see Isaiah 11:1-2; Jeremiah 23:5, 33:15).

    iii. *What, therefore, does Pilate unwittingly reveal about Jesus by presenting him to the people with the words, "Behold, the man…"?*

    Pilate is the unconscious prophet. By saying, "Behold, the man," Pilate unwittingly presents Jesus as the royal king Zechariah foretold.

6. *At the turning point in Christ's trial before Pilate, the chief priests say, "We have no king but Caesar" (John 19:14-15).*

a. *Read **Judges 8:23** and **1 Samuel 8:7**. According to these passages, who is the true king of Israel?*

God is the true king of Israel.

b. *Read **Deuteronomy 17:15**. According to this law, what kind of rulers are prohibited to rule Israelites?*

The people of Israel are to have no foreigner ruling over them.

c. *The chief priests are supposed to be the faithful representatives of God's people. What does this background tell us about the chief priests' words, "We have no king but Caesar"?*

God alone is king, and he rules the people through his appointed Davidic dynasty (see 2 Samuel 7:11-16). For the chief priests—the representatives of God's people—to say, "We have no king but Caesar" not only shows disregard for God's Law but also shows how they reject God as the one true king of Israel. Instead of choosing God or God's anointed Davidic King (Jesus), the chief priests claim the Roman emperor, who has been oppressing the Jewish people, as their king!

7. Read **Matthew 27:24**, *where Pilate washes his hands to distance himself from the guilt of Christ's innocent blood. Consider how the following passages might shed light on Pilate's action from a biblical perspective:*

    a. ***Psalm 26:6***

       "I wash my hands in innocence." That is what Pilate is trying to do; symbolically wipe his hands clean of Christ's unjust crucifixion.

    b. ***Deuteronomy 21:1-9*** *(a passage prescribing certain rituals for when a body is found but the murderer is unknown)*

       The elders nearest to where the murder occurred are to sacrifice a heifer and wash their hands, saying, "Our hands did not shed this blood" (Deuteronomy 21:7). This is similar to what Pilate does when he washes his hands and says, "I am innocent of this righteous man's blood" (Matthew 27:24).

D. Application

Facilitators: If time allows, invite group members to share their responses from this session's application questions.

After sharing your responses in the small group, watch Edward Sri's video presentation on
Session Three – The Trial Before Pilate: Jesus Is Condemned to Death.

THE DEATH OF THE MESSIAH

Jesus Carries His Cross, Is Crucified, and Dies

Facilitators: Read these responses to the questions ahead of time to help you prepare to lead the small-group discussion.

Participants: Reinforce what you have learned by reviewing these responses after your small-group discussion and before you continue to the next session.

A. Establish the Context

Facilitators: Take a moment to establish the context and what was learned in the previous session.

B. Read the Story

Facilitators: Ask someone to summarize the readings for this session. Begin your small-group discussion with a brief prayer.

C. Take a Deeper Look

Facilitators: If there is time, have someone read each passage aloud before it is discussed.

1. *Simon of Cyrene carries the Cross for Jesus.*

    a. *Read **Luke 23:26**. What does Luke tell us about the way Simon of Cyrene carried Christ's cross?*

    Simon carried the Cross "behind" Jesus.

    b. *According to what Jesus teaches in the following verses, what must one do to be a disciple?*

        i. ***Luke 9:23***

        "If any man would come after me, let him deny himself and take up his cross daily and follow me."

        ii. ***Luke 14:27***

        "Whoever does not bear his own cross and come after me, cannot be my disciple."

    c. *What might this background tell us about Simon of Cyrene?*

    Luke emphasizes that to be a disciple means taking up the Cross and following Jesus. Luke gives us a visual aid of this in Simon of Cyrene, a man who is given Christ's cross and carries it behind Jesus. In other words, he takes up the Cross and follows Christ. Luke subtly portrays Simon of Cyrene as a disciple. This small detail would support the early tradition that Simon was transformed through his encounter with the Cross and eventually became a Christian.

2. *Jesus tells the women of Jerusalem not to weep (see Luke 23:28).*

    a. *Read the following passages in which Jesus tells others not to weep. Why does he tell them not to weep?*

        i. ***Luke 7:11-17***

        Jesus tells the mourners not to weep because he is going to raise the woman's son from the dead.

        ii. ***Luke 8:49-55***

        Jesus tells the mourners not to weep because he is going to raise Jairus' daughter from the dead.

    b. *With this background in mind, why do you think Jesus tells the women of Jerusalem not to weep for him?*

    Jesus, the one who can raise the dead, is also able to raise himself from the dead. They do not need to weep for him because he will rise on Easter.

3. *Psalm 22 is about a righteous man who is being persecuted by his enemies. His experiences prefigure in many ways what Christ endures on Calvary.*

    a. *Read **Psalm 22:16-18**. What are two or three points made in these three verses that foreshadow what happens to Jesus when he first gets to Calvary?*

    The evil doers have pierced the man's hands and feet, just as the soldiers pierce Christ's hands and feet to the Cross (see Luke 24:39, John 20:25).

    The man's enemies divide his garments by casting lots, just as the soldiers do for Christ's garments (see Matthew 27:35).

    The wicked "stare and gloat over" the righteous man in Psalm 22, just as the soldiers "kept watch over" Jesus at Calvary (Matthew 27:36).

    b. *Read **Psalm 22:7-8**. How do these verses prophetically foreshadow Christ's experience as he is hanging on the Cross?*

    The man's enemies "wag their heads" just as the people passing by Calvary are "wagging their heads" (Matthew 27:39).

    The wicked mock the righteous man in Psalm 22:8, saying, "He committed his cause to the LORD; let him deliver him, let him rescue him, for he delights in him!" This foreshadows what the chief priests at Calvary say: "He trusts in God; let God deliver him now, if he desires him" (Matthew 27:43).

4. *Read **Matthew 27:45**, which tells how from noon until 3 PM, a great darkness covered the earth. Read the following passages from the Old Testament and explain how they each prefigure this darkness on Good Friday.*

    a. ***Exodus 10:22***

    A thick darkness covered all the land of Egypt for "three days" just as a thick darkness covered all the land for three hours on Good Friday.

    b. ***Amos 8:9-10***

    Amos foretells how God will make the sun go down at noon, darkening the earth "in broad daylight," which is what happens on Good Friday (Matthew 27:45).

    He also foretells how God will "turn your feasts into mourning," which points to how the feast of Passover will become a day of mourning over Christ's death.

    He also foretells how the mourning will be like that over the sorrow for an only son—pointing to the mourning over God's only beloved Son being killed on Calvary.

5. *John's Gospel presents Jesus' sacrifice on Calvary in light of the Passover sacrifice.*

   a. *What do the following verses tell us about the Passover?*

      i. *Exodus 12:21-23*

      The Passover lamb is to be sacrificed, and a hyssop is to be dipped into the blood of the Passover lamb and then raised up to mark the doorposts of the Israelites' homes with the lamb's blood.

      ii. *Exodus 12:46*

      The bones of the Passover lamb are not to be broken.

      iii. *Numbers 9:9-12*

      The bones of the Passover lamb are not to be broken.

   b. *How do the following verses from Christ's passion remind us of the Passover lamb? (Note that the Passover lambs were slaughtered on the day of preparation before Passover around noon.)*

      i. *John 19:14*

      Jesus is condemned to be crucified at the sixth hour (noon), which is around the time the Passover lambs would have been sacrificed.

      ii. *John 19:29*

      Hyssop is used to bring Jesus the vinegary wine to his mouth. This recalls the hyssop dipped in the Passover lamb's blood and used to mark the Israelites' doorposts.

      iii. *John 19:32-33*

      John notes how the soldiers did not break Jesus' legs as they did for the other crucified men that day. Jesus is just like the Passover lamb whose legs were not to be broken. Jesus is like the Passover lambs sacrificed for the people.

6. *Read **John 19:34**. How was this event foreshadowed by prophets in the following passages?*

   a. *Zechariah 12:10*

   Zechariah foretells how God will send a spirit of compassion on the people of Jerusalem "when they look on him whom they have pierced"—a prophecy that foreshadows how the soldiers will pierce Christ's side.

   b. *Luke 2:33-35*

   When the forty-day old Jesus was presented in the Temple as a baby, the elderly Simeon gives a prophecy to Mary about how Jesus will be misunderstood, opposed, and plotted against. He foretells that "a sword" will pierce Jesus, and it will pierce Mary's soul also. That prophecy is fulfilled in the soldier's piercing Christ's side.

7. *God is sometimes called the God of second chances. One character who appears at Jesus' death is one who got a second chance with Jesus. His name is Nicodemus.*

    a. *Read **John 3:1**. Who is Nicodemus? How much faith and understanding should we expect from such a man?*

        Nicodemus is a Pharisee and a "ruler of the Jews," meaning he is a member of the Sanhedrin. We would expect him to understand the Scriptures and Jesus' teachings.

    b. *Read **John 3:2-10**. What impression do you have of Nicodemus from these verses? How well does he understand Jesus?*

        Nicodemus comes to Jesus at night (see John 3:2), which is not a good sign. It is as if he is hiding, afraid of what others might think of him if he is seen talking to Jesus. Judas will later leave the Last Supper to betray Jesus "at night" (13:30).

        One of Nicodemus' problems is that he views Jesus merely as a "teacher" (John 3:2). He fails to see what others in John's Gospel have already seen in Jesus—that he is the "lamb of God" (John 1:29), "the Messiah" (John 1:41), and the "Son of God" and "King of Israel" (John 1:49).

        Nicodemus also seems very confused. He misunderstands Jesus. Jesus talks about being spiritually "born anew," but Nicodemus takes him literally: "How can a man be born when he is old? Can he enter a second time into his mother's womb and be born?" (John 3:4). Jesus upbraids this "teacher of Israel" because he does not understand (John 3:10).

    c. *Read **John 7:45-52**. What is your impression of Nicodemus in this scene? Do you think there has been a change in him?*

        Nicodemus defends Jesus against his own Pharisees who want Jesus arrested without a fair hearing. He says, "Does our law judge a man without first giving him a hearing and learning what he does?" (John 7:51).

    d. *Read **John 19:39-42** and **John 12:1-5**. Compare Nicodemus' gift with Mary of Bethany's generosity. What does this tell you about Nicodemus' faith and devotion to Jesus?*

        To anoint Jesus' feet, Mary of Bethany gave a generous one-pound gift of myrrh that had been worth 300 denarii (see John 12:5). That was seen as extravagant. Nicodemus' gift of 100 pounds, therefore, may have been worth 30,000 denarii. He takes the generosity to a whole new level and gives Jesus a burial that was fit for a king.

D. Application

Facilitators: If time allows, invite group members to share their responses from this session's application questions.

After sharing your responses in the small group, watch Edward Sri's video presentation on
Session Four – The Death of the Messiah: Jesus Carries His Cross, Is Crucified, and Dies.

NO
GREATER
LOVE

THE SEVEN LAST WORDS
Jesus the Teacher at Calvary

Facilitators: Read these responses to the questions ahead of time to help you prepare to lead the small-group discussion.

Participants: Reinforce what you have learned by reviewing these responses after your small-group discussion and before you continue to the next session.

A. Establish the Context

Facilitators: Take a moment to establish the context and what was learned in the previous session.

B. Read the Story

Facilitators: Ask someone to summarize the readings for this session. Begin your small-group discussion with a brief prayer.

C. Take a Deeper Look

Facilitators: If there is time, have someone read each passage aloud before it is discussed.

1. *Read **Luke 23:34**.*

   a. *What are the first of the last words of Christ?*

   "Father, forgive them; for they know not what they do."

   b. *What did Jesus teach in the following verses?*

      i. ***Matthew 5:7***

      "Blessed are the merciful, for they shall obtain mercy."

      ii. ***Matthew 5:43-45***

      "Love your enemies and pray for those who persecute you."

      iii. ***Luke 11:4***

      In the Our Father prayer, Jesus teaches us to pray, "Forgive us our sins, for we ourselves forgive everyone who is indebted to us."

      iv. ***Matthew 18:21-23***

      We should be willing to forgive those who sin against us seven times seventy times, meaning always.

   c. *How might these other teachings of Jesus relate to what Jesus says from the Cross in **Luke 23:34**?*

   Throughout his public ministry, Jesus taught his disciples to be merciful and willing to forgive—to love our enemies, even praying for the people who persecute us. He taught us in the Our Father that we will be forgiven to the extent that we forgive others. Jesus certainly modeled his teachings on mercy and loving and praying for one's enemies in the first of his last words from the Cross. He does not cry out in anger against his persecutors. His first words are to forgive them.

2. *Read **Luke 23:43**.*

   a. *What are the second of the last words of Christ?*

   "Today you will be with me in Paradise."

   b. *Read **Luke 23:42**. What did the good thief ask from Jesus?*

   To be remembered when Jesus enters into his kingdom.

c. *Read **Luke 23:43**. What did Jesus offer him? Was this what the good thief asked for, or something more, or something less?*

Jesus offers him much more than he asked for. The man asked simply to be remembered. Jesus says the good thief will be with Jesus and offers him paradise! As St. Ambrose said, "More abundant is the favor shown than the request made."[9] Commenting further on this passage, Ambrose explains the significance of Jesus saying that the good thief will be with him: "Life is to be with Christ; for where Christ is, there is the kingdom."[10]

3. *Read **John 19:26-27**.*

a. *What are the third of the last words of Christ?*

"Woman, behold, your son! ... Behold, your mother!"

b. *Read the following verses. What do they each tell us about the beloved disciple?*

i. ***John 13:25***

He rests on Jesus' breast at the Last Supper.

ii. ***John 19:26***

He is the only one of the twelve apostles to be with Jesus at Calvary.

iii. ***John 20:8***

He is the first to the tomb and to believe in the risen Jesus.

iv. ***John 21:7***

He is the first apostle to bear witness to the risen Christ.

v. ***John 21:24***

He continues to bear witness to Christ.

---

[9] St. Ambrose, *Exposition on the Gospel of Luke*, 10.121.
[10] Ibid.

c. *Some saints and scholars have seen the beloved disciple not only as an individual disciple, but the model disciple—one who represents all faithful disciples. How might the overall picture of the beloved disciple in John's Gospel support this interpretation?*

In John's Gospel, individual characters often represent larger groups. For example, the Samaritan woman who comes to believe in Jesus is seen as representing the many Samaritans who come to believe in him. Nicodemus the Pharisee is confused and in the dark about Jesus, representing the many Pharisees who do not understand Christ. The same is true with the beloved disciple.

The beloved disciple is traditionally understood to be the individual St. John, the one apostle in the fourth Gospel whose name is not mentioned—he is simply referred to as "the beloved disciple." Still, this individual disciple stands out in John's Gospel as a model disciple. He is close to Jesus at the Last Supper, and he is faithful to Jesus, going all the way to the Cross when the others ran away out of fear. He is the first to believe in the risen Christ, and he bears witness to Jesus. As a result, he can be seen as representing all faithful disciples—all those who faithfully follow Jesus closely and bear witness to him.

d. *If the beloved disciple represents all faithful disciples, what does it mean for us that Jesus says to him, "Behold, your mother!" (John 19:27)?*

When Mary is given a special maternal relationship with the beloved disciple, this tells us a lot about Mary's relationship with all of us believers. John 19:25-27 reveals that Mary becomes the mother of the beloved disciple. But remember, the beloved disciple himself represents all faithful disciples. Therefore, this scene can support the Catholic understanding of Mary's spiritual motherhood. Since the beloved disciple represents all of us, it is as if Jesus is saying to us what he said to the beloved disciple on Good Friday: "Behold, your mother!" Jesus thinks of us shortly before he dies and gives us one last great gift: the gift of his mother Mary. And as our spiritual mother, Mary constantly prays for us like a loving mother.

4. *Read **Matthew 27:46**.*

    a. *What are the fourth of the last words of Christ?*

      "My God, My God, why have you forsaken me?"

    b. *In these words, Jesus is quoting from Psalm 22. Consider the background of this Psalm.*

      i. *Read **Psalm 22:1-2**. How does this shed light on what Jesus was facing on Good Friday?*

      The person in this psalm experiences great anguish—so much so that he feels as if he has been abandoned by God. Jesus quotes this line from Psalm 22 because he finds himself in a similar situation.

      ii. *Read **Psalm 22:3-4** and **Psalm 22:9-11**. Do these verses sound like a man in despair or a man with hope even in distress? Explain.*

      As Psalm 22 moves on into verses 3-4, we see that the suffering man turns to God in confidence. He remembers how God has been faithful to his ancestors when they were facing great trials: "In you our fathers trusted, they trusted, and you delivered them … in you they trusted and were not disappointed." God's faithfulness in the past is a cause of hope and strength for him in the present. If God delivered his ancestors in their times of affliction, God can deliver him as well.

      iii. *Read **Psalm 22:23-28**. How does the man in this psalm conclude with great confidence that God will come to rescue him from his afflictions?*

      The psalm reaches its climax in these verses. The suffering man sees that his suffering has a purpose and will bear fruit. In the end, he proclaims how all the families of the earth will turn to the Lord, and God will rule over all nations.

      iv. *What might this background tell us about what Jesus meant by quoting from Psalm 22?*

      Jesus quotes the opening line from Psalm 22 ("My God, my God, why have you forsaken me?") to bring to mind the theme of the whole psalm—the theme of God rescuing those who cry out to him for help in their afflictions. In Psalm 22, a persecuted, suffering righteous man who feels as if he is abandoned by God places his trust in the Lord who will deliver him. And God is faithful, rescuing the man and inspiring all the nations to turn to the Lord and worship him. By quoting the first line of Psalm 22, Jesus is saying he is like that righteous man being persecuted. He is the one suffering at the hands of his enemies. But like the psalmist, Jesus entrusted himself to the Father, confident that he will be rescued on the third day.

5. Read *John 19:28*.

    a. *What are the fifth of the last words of Christ?*

        "I thirst."

    b. *Read the following Old Testament passages and explain how they foreshadow Christ's thirst on the Cross.*

        i. **Psalm 69:21**

            "For my thirst they gave me vinegar to drink."

            This foreshadows how Jesus was thirsty on the Cross and how the soldiers give him the vinegary wine to drink.

        ii. **Psalm 22:15**

            "My strength is dried up like a potsherd, and my tongue cleaves to my jaws; you lay me in the dust of death."

            This foreshadows how thirsty Jesus probably was, having been beaten, scourged, crucified, and hanging on the Cross for six hours.

    c. *Read John 4:7. Here we see Jesus expressed his thirst once before. But as the* Catechism of the Catholic Church *explains, he thirsts for more than water; he thirsts for us: "Jesus thirsts; his asking arises from the depths of God's desire for us. Whether we realize it or not, prayer is the encounter of God's thirst with ours. God thirsts that we may thirst for him"* (CCC 2560). *How does this view of Jesus' "thirst" change the way you look at prayer?*

        Answers will vary, but one point to draw out is how prayer is not just our work, our words, or our performance in the chapel. Jesus seeks us first. He thirsts for us—for our time, our attention, our love. Jesus longs for us.

6. Read *John 19:30*.

    a. *What are the sixth of the last words of Christ?*

        "It is finished."

    b. *Read the following verses and explain what Jesus says he is bringing to completion:*

        i. **John 4:34**

            Jesus says, "My food is to do the will of him who sent me, and to accomplish his work."

        ii. **John 17:4**

            Jesus prays to the Father saying he finished the work the Father gave him to do.

c. *With this background in mind, what do you think Jesus means when he says from the Cross, "It is finished"?*

"It is finished" is not a "game over" moment for Jesus. It is not merely the end of something, but rather the completion of something—the accomplishment of the Father's plan. These words represent the victorious proclamation that Jesus has brought to completion all that the Father sent him to do. He has accomplished the Father's plan from the beginning to bring salvation to the world.

7. Read **Luke 23:46**.

a. *What are the seventh of the last words of Christ?*

"Father, into your hands I commit my spirit!"

b. *Read **Luke 9:44**. Into whose hands did Jesus predict he would be handed over?*

Jesus predicted he would be given into the hands of men—a reference to how he will be arrested in the garden of Gethsemane and handed over to the chief priests.

c. *Read **Luke 23:46**. Ultimately, into whose hands does Jesus entrust his spirit?*

In the end, Jesus is not handed over to his enemies. In fact, he is not passively handed over to anyone. In his last moment before dying, he is the one acting; he actively hands his spirit to someone: "I commit my spirit." Jesus commits his spirit to his Father's hands, not the hands of his enemies.

d. *Read the following verses and explain what they tell us about the Father's hands:*

i. ***John 10:27-29***

The Father's hands are trustworthy and protect the sheep. No one is able to snatch the sheep out of the Father's hands.

ii. *Acts 4:26-28*

God's hand is associated with his plan—his providential plan for the salvation of the world. God can bring good from evil. God could use the greatest evil—the crucifixion of the Son of God—to bring about the greatest good: the redemption of the human family. On Good Friday, therefore, even the enemies of Jesus—Herod and Pilate—"do whatever your hand and your plan had predestined to take place."

iii. *Acts 4:29-30*

Here, God's hand is associated with healing and miracles. The apostles prayed for God to stretch out his hand to heal and perform signs and wonders among the believers. And as they prayed, they all were filled with the Holy Spirit.

e. *What does this background tell us about the confidence Jesus must have had in entrusting his spirit into his Father's hands?*

At his dying moment, Jesus is not a passive victim, running out of time, breath, and life. He actively commits his spirit to the Father. At the start of his passion, Jesus was given to his enemies' hands. But in the end, we see he entrusts himself into his Father's hands—hands which are faithful and protective, never allowing the sheep to be taken away. The Father's hands also point to the Father's plan and his healing power. By entrusting his spirit to his Father's hands, Jesus expresses great confidence that the Father will not allow him to be taken away but will protect him and rescue him from his enemies. His words point to how his death is not a random act of evil, but all part of the Father's plans, and the Father will use it for good, for healing and to lead to the greatest sign—the Resurrection—all to bring about the salvation of the world.

D. Application

Facilitators: If time allows, invite group members to share their responses from this session's application questions.

After sharing your responses in the small group, watch Edward Sri's video presentation on
Session Five – The Seven Last Words: Jesus the Teacher at Calvary

Understand What We Say and Do in the **Liturgy**

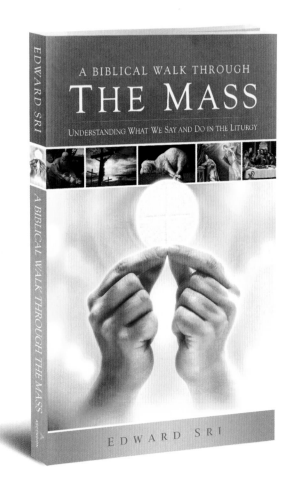

A Biblical Walk Through the Mass by Edward Sri

As Catholics, the Mass is the center of our Faith. We celebrate it every day. We know all the responses. We know all the gestures. But do we know what it all means?

In *A Biblical Walk Through the Mass*, Dr. Sri takes us on a unique tour of the Liturgy. This book explores the biblical roots of the words and gestures we experience in the Mass and explains their profound significance. This intriguing book will renew your faith and deepen your devotion to the Eucharist.